A YOUNG PERSON'S GUIDE TO
SCIENCE

ALSO BY ROY A. GALLANT

A YOUNG PERSON'S GUIDE TO
SCIENCE
Ideas That Change the World

ROY A. GALLANT

MACMILLAN PUBLISHING COMPANY   NEW YORK

MAXWELL MACMILLAN CANADA   TORONTO

MAXWELL MACMILLAN INTERNATIONAL
NEW YORK   OXFORD   SINGAPORE   SYDNEY

FOR MELISSA,

who must learn to care for this planet
in ways that we have not

1   3   5   7   9   10   8   6   4   2

The text of this book is set in 11 pt. Meridien. Art on pages 22, 35, 40–41, 52–53, 84, 88, 112, 114–115, 116, 125, 129, 170, and 198–199 by Robert Bull Design. *Photo Credits:* page 1 © Hal Jandorf, courtesy of NASA; page 47 by Constance Ftera; page 65 © Keith R. Porter/Photo Researchers, Inc.; page 121 courtesy of Hale Observatories; page 185 courtesy of NASA. Book design by Jean Krulis.

Library of Congress Cataloging-in-Publication Data
Gallant, Roy A.
    A young person's guide to science : ideas that change the world / Roy A. Gallant.—1st ed.
        p.   cm.
    Includes bibliographical references and index.
    Summary: Covers a broad spectrum of topics in the physical and life sciences to provide a foundation of basic scientific knowledge.
    ISBN 0-02-735775-9
    1. Science—Miscellanea—Juvenile literature.   [1. Science—Miscellanea.]   I. Title.
Q163G27   1993   500—dc20   92-12332

ACKNOWLEDGMENTS

I wish to thank Macmillan Publishing Company for permission to incorporate in this book brief adaptations of earlier works by the author: *The Peopling of Planet Earth, Before the Sun Dies,* and *Earth's Vanishing Forests,* copyright by Roy A. Gallant. My thanks also to Franklin Watts, publisher of *Restless Earth,* copyright by Roy A. Gallant; and to the National Geographic Society, publisher of *Our Universe,* copyright by the National Geographic Society.

Special thanks are due Dr. Edward J. Kormondy, Professor of Biology and Chancellor of the University of Hawaii at Hilo, for his many valuable comments in the course of reviewing the manuscript for Chapters 1, 2, 3, 4, 5, and 7 of this book. And my gratitude to Dr. Jerry LaSala, physicist and astronomer at the University of Southern Maine, Portland, for his comments on Chapter 6.

Do not think for a moment that you know the real atom. The atom is an idea, a theory, a hypothesis. It is whatever you need to account for the facts of experience. (As our ideas about the atom have changed in the past, so will they continue to change in the future.) An idea in science, remember, lasts only as long as it is useful.

—Alfred Romer

CONTENTS

Three   UNDERSTANDING THE ENVIRONMENT

Four   THE HUMAN ORGANISM

Five HUMAN BEHAVIOR

Six THE PHYSICAL WORLD

Seven SCIENCE AND HUMAN VALUES

MANAGING OURSELVES

MANAGING THE PLANET

PREFACE

The regrettable state of scientific literacy of young people—and adults—in the United States began to stir the nation's awareness and concern around 1988. According to the American Association for the Advancement of Science (AAAS) report, Science for All Americans, "The terms and circumstances of human existence can be expected to change radically during the next human life span. Science, mathematics, and technology will be at the center of that change—causing it, shaping it, responding to it. Therefore, they will be essential to the education of today's children for tomorrow's world."

Unhappily, too few of today's young people in the United States are getting an education that promotes a basic knowledge of what science is and the growing number of ways it touches our lives. "A cascade of studies has made it abundantly clear that by both national standards and international norms, U.S. education is failing the nation," says the AAAS.

According to a *Scientific American* article, "The evidence is clear: American students are technologically illiterate, possessing few if any of the mathematics and science skills needed to function successfully in the world today or as it will be in future decades. Comparisons of test scores show that U.S. students lag behind their counterparts in much of the Western world in science and mathematics. Worse, their scores in these critical disciplines show no improvement." One in four of us believes in ghosts and astrology.

One sixth of the population claims to have communicated with the dead, and one in seven reports having seen a flying saucer (up from one in ten about fifteen years ago).

In other parts of the world, as well as in the United States, science is losing prestige and relevance in the minds of many. In Russia, for instance, science and rational thought are being eroded by occultism, which does "not bode well for a free society," says Loren Graham, a historian of Soviet science at Harvard University.

To deny that science touches our lives is absurd. Can we deny that the microscope and telescope have changed the ways in which we view ourselves and the Universe? Ultimately, science touches us most deeply by changing human values. Science continually introduces new ideas into culture, and thereby changes culture through the pressure of technological change. The invention of the wheel, the printing press, radio and television, computers, antibiotics, and genetic engineering are examples.

This book is a modest attempt to help reinforce young people's frail base of scientific knowledge (and that of the not-so-young). It presents the essence of a number of major ideas in the life sciences and the physical sciences, concepts that all of us should have a sound understanding of, if not a mastery over. A firm grasp of these and other concepts in science is crucial to our ability to formulate reasoned and informed courses of action that often are required of responsible citizens, young and old alike.

Here are only a few questions to test your scientific literacy:

- Can you explain why we should be concerned about a thinning of the ozone layer in Earth's atmosphere?
- You may have strong feelings about a government plan to use your state or county as a site for a radioactive waste dump, but could you explain to a group why such a plan should be opposed, or why it should be encouraged? Is it possible to take a rational and informed stand on the problems of radioactive waste management without understanding what radioactivity is, what it does, and how it is produced?

- Do you know enough about AIDS to carry on an informed discussion of whether a child with AIDS should or should not be allowed to attend public school?
- Examine this statement: "The cause of Earth's seasons is the changing distance of Earth from the Sun." Is the statement correct? If you think it is *not* correct, what is the correct explanation of seasons?

Why is it essential for science to challenge ideas about the physical universe that are based on authority rather than on investigation?

Why do virtually all scientists the world over accept the principal of evolution and see evolution as the unifying force of all biology? Until 1990, the state of Texas prohibited the teaching of evolution in its schools from the earliest grades through high school. Instead, Texas officials favored the authoritarian biblical explanation of the formation of Earth and its varied life forms. Because Texas buys 9 percent of the public school science textbooks, publishers—who are in business to make money, not to educate children—avoided any mention of evolution in their books. So Texas was able to dictate what a large number of U.S. teenagers were taught, or not taught, about biology. Consequently, students were deprived of learning what evolution is and how it works.

Can you explain why science is unable to prove or disprove the existence of God, the accuracy of astrology, and other aspects of the supernatural?

Why are ecologists profoundly concerned about the rapid growth of the world's human population? How many environmental problems are directly linked with overpopulation?

Do your parents or grandparents know the difference between a star and a planet? Do you? Is the Sun a star or a planet?

This book is not a random collection of trivial questions. It is not a catalog of facts to be committed to memory. Instead, it is a careful orchestration of many basic concepts in science, ideas that people who consider themselves educated should know. The book also is intended to broaden and strengthen what may be a foggy understanding of certain fundamental scientific ideas.

Without a sufficient understanding of these ideas we risk having to sit by passively while others make up our minds for us about matters that can change our lives. Whenever that happens, we should have the uneasy feeling that in some small but important way we have lost a measure of control over our lives.

One

HOW SCIENCE WORKS AND HOW WE USE IT

THE SCIENTIFIC WORLD VIEW

Science, as a method of investigating the world, began whenever and wherever common sense was challenged. The Greek philosopher Aristotle spoke contemptuously of common sense, saying that it was neither common nor sense.

The phrase, "seeing is believing," is an example of common sense: The stars, Sun, and Moon are *seen* to parade endlessly in great circles across the sky and around a motionless Earth. Modern Western science can be said to have begun when that false impression was replaced with the scientific knowledge that Earth is not motionless and is not at the center of the Universe. (That the Earth does move and is not the center of the Universe was proposed by the Greek astronomer Aristarchus around 250 B.C.)

People of long ago invented tales or myths that served as substitutes for natural causes to explain events that they could not understand. If an answer was not readily at hand, the mythmakers invented one. Over the centuries, myths by the millions have been handed down from parent to offspring to explain how life began, why earthquakes occur, and why the apparent motions of the stars and planets influence our lives. If belief in the supernatural did not provide enlightenment, it nevertheless provided peace of mind.

In today's language we would say that myths served as models that convincingly accounted for what people could observe of the world. While the model continued to work, all was well. But ancient Greek scholars

3

rejected myths, superstition, and the supernatural in explaining natural events. Instead, they relied on purely natural causes to account for all observable changes, motions, and the very matter that made up the physical universe.

Attaining scientific knowledge became the goal, and a number of important areas emerged from that "Golden Age of Learning." One was that careful and systematic observation of events would reveal patterns in nature, including: regular and recurring changes of the Moon's phases, observed changes in motion of the planets among the background stars, the predictable changes in seasons, and the cause of day and night. The very regularity and, therefore, predictability of such events were evidence that natural forces, not the gods, controlled the events. The gods, after all, were as erratic as humans and as much controlled by their emotions of jealousy, greed, love, hate, and envy. If in doubt, read any myth. If the gods controlled natural events, we could expect to live in a universe characterized by whimsy rather than consistent patterns.

Another important idea of the early Greek period was the notion that the world is knowable. Although the Greeks knew little chemistry or physics, they were excellent mathematicians. Aristarchus used geometry to estimate Earth's distance from the Moon and Sun. His answers were a bit wide of the mark, but his line of *thinking* was correct. An estimate of Earth's circumference by another scholar (Eratosthenes) was better, off by only 130 miles. The scholars of ancient Greece realized that the human ability to reason, accompanied by a genius for invention, would lead to knowledge of ever greater precision. It would also lead to a world view characterized by change and no longer dependent on common sense, tradition, or authority.

HUNCHES, THEORIES, AND LAWS

One of the most exciting discoveries we can make is that knowledge is interesting and wonderful. One day a crystal or a butterfly mysteriously catches your mind, and you regard the object in a new way—noticing that it is not like other crystals or other butterflies. You then begin to wonder why this object is different from other objects like it. How is it made? How does it work? A flood of these and more questions opens a new world—knowledge has become interesting. Clumsily at first, but then with greater ease and skill, you discover that there are wonderful and mysterious connections between things. You have begun to develop a scientific world view.

Later in life natural curiosity about the world and opportunities for learning about it are sharpened by training and practice. The intense curiosity of scientists makes them want more than just everyday explanations. They search endlessly for answers to the questions "Why?" and "How?"

A scientist's method for finding out about things does not follow a narrow path of inquiry. Although different scientists often work in different ways, all have certain thinking habits in common. They begin with what little they already know about whatever it is they are investigating. They then make a hunch, or advance a beginning explanation called a hypothesis. For example, people once thought Earth was flat because that is what their eyes told them. But the Greek philospher Aristotle observed that during an eclipse of the Moon Earth's shadow line was seen to be curved, not straight. That suggested to Aristotle the hypothesis that Earth is a sphere.

Once they have formalized a hunch into a hypothesis, scientists make more observations (or do experiments) to see whether the hypothesis holds up. Aristotle observed that the mast of a departing ship appears shorter and shorter as the ship sails away. This was further evidence that Earth is curved.

When enough evidence has been collected and if it continues to support the hypothesis, the hypothesis is given greater status; it becomes a theory. Meanwhile, other scientists try to repeat the observations, or duplicate the experiments in order to test the hypothesis. A hypothesis that cannot be tested is of no scientific use. Further observations and experiments either support or challenge a theory. If evidence continues to support the theory, it becomes a scientific principle, or a scientific law. Among the most convincing evidence that Earth is a sphere are the numerous photographs of the planet taken from space. The first hypothesis suggesting that Earth is not flat could be stated as "Earth is round." With more advanced observation techniques, the hypothesis could be rephrased more precisely as

"Earth is a sphere." Today, with modern methods of measuring our planet, we can say with confidence that "Earth is an oblate spheroid," because measurements show that it is not exactly spherical.

Sometimes a hunch or a new bit of evidence suggests that a new hypothesis may better explain an event than a hypothesis that has been around for a while and has not been challenged. At other times new methods of observation show us that this or that piece of the Universe is not quite as we supposed it to be yesterday. At such times the scientist must be prepared to cast aside or revise an old "truth" and replace it with a new one. Or a new method of observation may confirm something that we had suspected but could not support with evidence. Or it may reveal something in such new and marvelous detail that suddenly there is an explanation where there had been none before.

The invention of two instruments, the telescope enabling us to view very distant celestial objects, and the microscope to see very minute organisms, in such detail that our understanding of the substance of stars or how living cells divide advanced by giant steps very quickly. All such revelations come under the heading of "scientific knowledge" because they can be tested, verified, or shown to be false. Science, then, is not a body of facts to be committed to memory. Rather, it is a way of looking at the world. To the curious mind, knowledge gained in that way is always interesting and wonderful.

WHY SCIENTISTS CONSTRUCT MODELS

How can we find out if pollution is affecting Earth's health? It would be fairly simple to find out if there were two Earths. We would simply carry on as we do now on this Earth and not change our ways. On the other Earth we could experiment by curbing air pollution for a while, then water pollution, and so on. We would then compare conditions on both Earths to find out what effects the changes had on the experimental Earth's environmental health. But because we do not have a second Earth to serve as an experimental model, we build a mathematical model and experiment with it instead.

A scientific model is a tool for thinking. Scientists are forever constructing such models. A model can be a simple word statement, such as "a star is a sphere of gases that increase in temperature, pressure, and density toward the center." Or a model can be a series of mathematical statements that describe how and why those three conditions increase toward a star's center. Or a model can be an explanation, part a drawing and part a chemical equation, of how a saltwater fish avoids taking in dangerously high amounts of salt. A model also can be an object, such as a physical model of an ice crystal that suggests how the crystal's atoms are arranged.

In the early 1800s the British astronomer Sir William Herschel became the first to model a shape for the universe of stars visible to him (our home galaxy, the Milky Way). By counting the number of stars seen in patches of sky in various directions, he concluded that our stellar home was shaped like a gigantic powder puff, with the Sun near the center.

Herschel's model was based on what he was able to observe, and as long as observation continued to verify the model, the model reflected scientific truth. Herschel's model withstood the test of time for about a hundred years. But new observation techniques eventually showed that although Herschel's model was correct in some ways (the galaxy's shape, for instance), it was incorrect in others (the Sun's position, for instance). Herschel's model had to be revised; sometimes a model must be thrown out completely. A scientific model reflects scientific truth as long as new evidence continues to verify the model; scientific truth rarely is permanent and unchanging.

WHY SCIENTISTS CONDUCT EXPERIMENTS

A scientist usually does an experiment not to prove or disprove something, but to find out what will happen. In the 1700s chemists held the hypothesis that things burned because they contained a mysterious substance called "phlogiston." The French chemist Antoine Lavoisier had a different idea of why things burned. It was not because they contained "phlogiston," he said, but because they combine with some "vital" part of the air. But what is that vital part? he asked himself.

To test his hypothesis, Lavoisier performed a series of carefully designed experiments that demonstrated beyond a doubt that oxygen, not phlogiston, caused burning. He was then able to restate his hypothesis about a "vital" part of the air causing burning: *Fire is caused by a chemical reaction between the burning substance and oxygen of the air.* In other words, combustion is rapid oxidation. And to this day no one has been able to produce evidence that burning occurs differently.

Experiments often reveal new facts that had not been predicted. The new facts lead to new hypotheses. Seldom does a scientist feel comfortable about the scientific truth of new knowledge until several different experiments have been performed, including experiments performed by other scientists.

Science is an endless search for knowledge that sometimes reveals the laws or rules of nature—how objects move through space, how this or that disease originates, how certain of our characteristics are passed on from parent to offspring in predictable patterns. To the scientist, the quest for this knowledge—the endless search for nature's rules—is the most important of life's undertakings.

SCIENCE VERSUS PSEUDOSCIENCE

Astrology is the study of presumed relationships between celestial objects (Sun, Moon, planets, and stars) and earthly events. Because the various hypotheses of astrology cannot be tested by experiment, science is unable to prove or disprove the claims of astrologers. Because astrology cannot be subjected to the methods of observation, analysis, prediction, and verification required by scientific inquiry, astrology is considered a pseudoscience, meaning "false" science.

Astrology started in ancient Babylonia some 3,000 or more years ago, and gradually spread to China, India, and Western cultures. Astrological charts are based on the ancient and erroneous belief that Earth is the center of the Universe. Astrology fails to recognize the astronomical fact that the Sun's apparent position in relation to the constellations changes continuously. Modern astrologers dismiss these observed facts, saying that such actual celestial events are not important. They contend that it is not the planets, Sun, Moon, and stars themselves that influence earthly affairs; instead, it is what those bodies "symbolize." Scientists cannot accept that explanation, because the notion cannot be tested.

Astrologers claim that their ancient art can be used to determine the probabilities of: weather patterns; body and intellectual types among individuals; good or ill fortune for nations, states, corporations, the Empire State Building, the Hoover Dam, or a given space shuttle launch; and the behavior of goldfish or other pets.

Astrology is an indoor activity and has nothing whatsoever to do with the physical reality of celestial objects. *Astronomy*, on the other hand, is the scientific study of the motions, composition, structure, and interactions of all celestial objects that make up the Universe. The science of astronomy grew out of early astrological observations at a time when *astrologers* actually made observations and recorded the changing positions of the planets, Sun, and Moon among the background stars. Astrology and astronomy parted ways more than 2,000 years ago in ancient Greece when Greek thinkers replaced superstition and belief in the gods with scientific inquiry, which was free of authority and prejudice.

Over the centuries astrology in the Western world has had periods of wide popularity and periods of scorn and condemnation. The Roman Church condemned astrology because it denies our freedom to determine and choose events in our lives. According to astrologers, events in our lives can be foretold by the stars and are beyond our control. This concept appeals to people who sometimes find it difficult to make important decisions that will affect their lives. Such people often seek mystical and spiritual guidance as a source of comfort instead of relying on their capacity for reason.

WHO'S WHO IN NATURE: CLASSIFYING LIVING THINGS

Any thinking person is curious about the world of living things. When you give a young child a box of marbles, blocks, and other such objects, the child probably will begin to sort the objects by separating all the round ones, or all the red ones, or all the blocks. Biologists do the same with living things, but their classification scheme is much more complex than that of the child. Biologists sort out the differences and similarities among living things by creating an all-inclusive card catalog that lists in the finest possible detail all observable differences and similarities among organisms. Systematics and taxonomy are the terms scientists use for their classification system.

The Greek philosopher Aristotle, who lived around 350 B.C., may have made the first large listing of organisms that were "plants" and others that were "animals." But those two kingdoms of organisms had been recognized much earlier.

The next attempt to sort out the staggering numbers of different kinds of plants and animals was made by the Swedish botanist Karl von Linne in the mid-1700s. His system of taxonomy is the one used today. It has three main features: (1) All scientific names of organisms are written in Latin, (2) each kind of organism (dogs, cats, oak trees) are assigned a two-word name, and (3) organisms are grouped in a descending order of categories that become ever narrower, as shown in the diagram that classifies your pet "Fido."

The category used most frequently is *species*, or the specific name of an organism. A species includes all the members of a population that commonly interbreed. There are millions of species—more than 300,000 species of beetles alone, more than 15,000 species of wild orchids. The species name consists of two parts: the genus name and the specific name. All human beings belong to the genus *Homo* and the species *sapiens*, written *Homo sapiens*, or abbreviated *H. sapiens*. "Homo" is Latin for man, and "sapiens" is Latin for wise. A red oak tree, for example, is classified as *Quercus rubrum*.

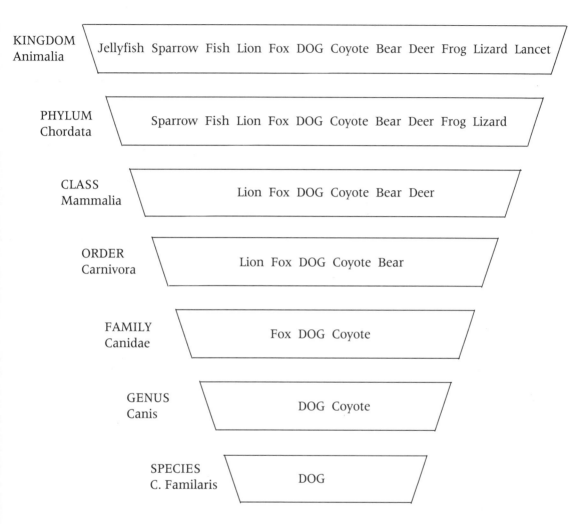

KINGDOM
Animalia
Jellyfish Sparrow Fish Lion Fox DOG Coyote Bear Deer Frog Lizard Lancet

PHYLUM
Chordata
Sparrow Fish Lion Fox DOG Coyote Bear Deer Frog Lizard

CLASS
Mammalia
Lion Fox DOG Coyote Bear Deer

ORDER
Carnivora
Lion Fox DOG Coyote Bear

FAMILY
Canidae
Fox DOG Coyote

GENUS
Canis
DOG Coyote

SPECIES
C. Familaris
DOG

Biologists classify organisms by their similarities. The animal *kingdom* includes all living animals, but excludes all plants and other non-animals. A smaller grouping is the *phylum*—in the example here, the phylum Chordata, which includes all animals with backbones. A next smaller grouping is *class*—mammals, for example. Each successively lower grouping contains a smaller number of organisms down to the *species* level, which contains only one kind of organism.

"Quercus" is Latin for oak, and "rubrum" is Latin for red. *Quercus alba* designates a white oak. *Canis familiaris* is Fido's scientific name. You probably can guess who *Felis domesticus* is.

Since the time of Linne (who, by the way, Latinized his own name to Carolus Linnaeus), additional categories have been added: phylum, family, and class, for example. The various categories are useful because each one provides certain information about the organisms within it. For instance, the subphylum Vertebrata tells you that all animals within it are vertebrates, or animals with backbones. And the order Carnivora tells you that all of its members are carnivorous, or meat-eating animals.

Today most biologists use the five-kingdom classification system, as opposed to the simpler and older two-kingdom system of animals (ANIMALIA) and plants (PLANTAE). The three more recent kingdoms are MONERA, PROTISTA, and FUNGI. They were added for several reasons, one of which is that the organisms assigned to these kingdoms are in some ways like animals and in other ways like plants.

The MONERA are single-cell organisms, such as bacteria and certain kinds (blue-green) of algae, that live alone or in colonies of many cells. They may move about or live attached to various objects. Their cells lack a definite cell control center called the nucleus. Some take in ready-made food from the environment. Others make their food by photosynthesis, as do all green plants. Viruses, which are not cells at all, also are classed as monerans.

The PROTISTA kingdom includes several groups of tiny organisms such as the single-cell amoeba, diatoms, green algae, and others. Some live alone, others live in colonies, and all have a definite nucleus. Some move about, others live attached. Some take in ready-made food from the environment, others make their own food.

The FUNGI kingdom includes slime molds and the various kinds of fungi, including mushrooms and toadstools. They all absorb ready-made food from the environment (dead organic matter), and most live attached. They have several nuclei that are scattered throughout the organism.

The PLANTAE kingdom is made up of organisms such as trees, shrubs, and the grasses. All have many cells, each with a well-defined nucleus control center and a tough cell wall that encloses a finer cell membrane and its fluid contents. Virtually all plants live rooted in the ground or attached to various objects. Their main source of food is the sugar glucose, which they manufacture through photosynthesis.

The ANIMALIA kingdom is made up of organisms such as elephants, mice, humans, and goldfish. All move about and contain many cells; each cell has a well-defined nucleus, but unlike plants, the cells do not have tough cell walls. Animals cannot make their own food; they obtain their nutrition by eating green plants or by eating other animals that eat green plants.

Two

THE LIVING WORLD

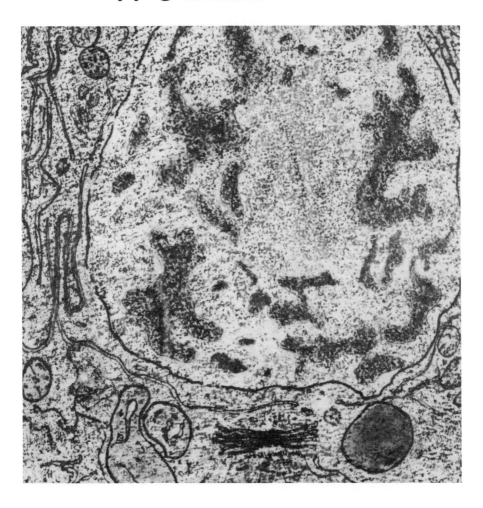

WHAT IS LIFE?

No one can deny that both nonliving things (such as a rock or a lump of Silly Putty) and living things are made up of atoms. Oxygen, hydrogen, nitrogen, phosphorus, carbon, potassium, calcium, and sodium are among the most important atoms in living matter. But rocks, water, salt, and many other nonliving substances contain some of the same kinds of atoms. What, then, is the difference between those things we call "living" and those we call "nonliving"? Consider the following statements: "Nonliving things cannot repair themselves if they are damaged." "Nonliving things cannot reproduce more of their kind." "Living things are able to survive drastic changes in their environment by responding to the environment and changing over many generations."

Electronics engineers and computer scientists would disagree with the first two statements and challenge the third one. They would say that they have designed machines that can repair themselves when damaged and can assemble out of an assortment of parts, the very parts they need for repair, even for growth. Perhaps so, in a limited way. But can they design a machine that can adapt to unpredictable changes in the environment over a period of millions of years? In other words, can they design a machine that evolves?

When we talk about differences between living and nonliving things, it is important to include *all* living matter—from the simplest one-cell organism to the elephant. The single cell and the elephant express their "aliveness" by endlessly organizing and reorganizing their billions of atoms from one moment to the next while remaining in a more or less steady chemical state. This process is something a piece of quartz, however well ordered its atoms may be, cannot do.

The qualities of matter that we collectively call "life" include:

(1) being packaged within a membrane or skin that acts as a defense against the disorderly outside world;

(2) a process, involving energy, that drives the many chemical activities that make new parts, repair worn or damaged parts, and generally maintain the organism from one minute to the next in a steady state;

(3) a way of obtaining nutrient molecules and energy from the outside environment, using that matter and energy for growth and maintenance, and eliminating waste molecules;

(4) a way of reproducing more whole organisms like itself, including more cells of its own pattern, and maintaining its orderly society of molecules amid the chaotic outside world.

Those are the activities of all living matter, from amoebas to zebras.

Although we can describe what living matter does and what it is made of, no one has yet come up with a satisfactory definition of life itself. In recent years a new branch of science, called "artificial life," has given the engineers and computer scientists a voice in our thoughts about the defining of life. They claim that they will soon be inventing living "artificial beings."

According to physicist J. Doyne Farmer, "Within the next century, we will likely witness the introduction on Earth of living organisms originally designed in large part by humans, but with the capability to reproduce and evolve just as natural organisms do."

Earth's chain of life began some 3.5 billion years ago. Since its beginning, that chain almost certainly has never been broken over the vast span of time. Perhaps giant asteroid impacts or other natural catastrophes from time to time have caused widespread extinctions of many groups of animals and plants, but the thread of life has persisted.

CELLS: THE SMALLEST UNITS OF LIVING MATTER

The smallest unit of living matter is the cell. Most cells are only a tiny fraction of an inch across (0.00004 in.), which is much smaller than the

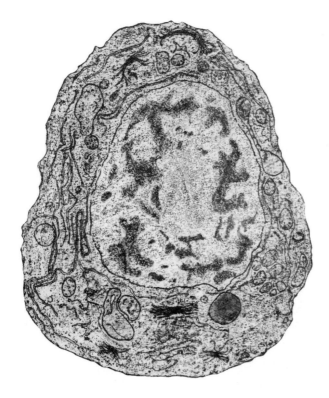

This drawing of a cell, magnified many thousands of times, shows that despite their size, cells are extremely complex. Each structure, enclosed within its own membrane sac, carries out one or more functions vital to the cell. And the number and distribution of the structures are continually changing to suit the cell's needs. By taking in materials from the outside, the cell keeps itself in repair, assembling new structures as they are needed.

(*Drawing by the author*)

dot over this letter *i*. Yet the tiniest cell is able to carry out all the chemical reactions that underlie the basic life functions—it grows, repairs itself when damaged, transforms matter into energy and energy back into matter, and reproduces more cells like itself. The chemical and physical mechanisms that drive these life processes are shared by all living things.

Cells are the chemical factories of life. If a vital part of a cell is damaged, and the damage is not major, the cell repairs itself by selecting from the outside the kinds and numbers of atoms and molecules it needs for repair. The cell then assembles new molecules of the right kind to make the repair.

Cells function and maintain themselves for as long as they are able to keep their atoms and molecules organized. "Organized" is a key word when we speak of living matter. From a cell's point of view, the outside world is a dangerous and disorderly collection of atoms and molecules. Just as the fluids of your body are protected from the harsh (dry) outside world by your skin, a cell's protection against the harsh (disorderly) outside world is "skin" in the form of a membrane sac. Without that membrane, the orderly arrangement of the cell's parts would be lost, and the cell would die instantly.

But a cell's membrane does not cut the cell off completely from its outside environment. All over the membrane are tiny openings. These tiny windows to the outside world let certain molecules enter the cell when they are needed. The windows also let waste molecules generated by the cell pass into the outside world. So there is a continual two-way flow of materials entering and leaving a cell as each cell exchanges matter with its outside environment.

Your body is made up of some 10 quadrillion (10,000,000,000,000,000) cells of about 100 different kinds. You have a stomach, brain, kidney, and other organs that work together and keep you alive; similarly, a cell has special parts, or organelles, each of which carries out special functions that keep the cell alive and healthy. In short, a cell can be described as a bag of watery fluid (cytoplasm) containing a variety of specialized organelles. Collectively, the cytoplasm and organelles are called protoplasm.

The nucleus is one such organelle, and it is the control center that directs the activity of a cell. The nuclear material is packaged within a thin membrane that allows exchange of certain materials with the rest of the cell. The control matter in the nucleus is the giant molecule DNA (*D*eoxyribo-*N*ucleic-*A*cid). DNA has two important functions: (1) it contains genes, those units of heredity that determine whether you are a tree, a mouse, or a person; and (2) it provides instructions that control the manufacture of proteins outside the nucleus in the cytoplasm. The instructions are given to the second most important material in the nucleus—RNA (*R*ibo-*N*ucleic-*A*cid). While the DNA stays within the nucleus, the RNA acts as a messenger that exits the nucleus. It attaches to the many organelles (ribosomes) in the cytoplasm where the manufacture of protein takes place.

A typical cell has about fifteen different kinds of organelles, and each kind is specialized for certain tasks. Organelles called mitochondria are the powerhouse of cells, because they generate energy-rich molecules that power a cell's endless chemical activity. Other organelles store food and waste products, or prepare a cell for division into two cells.

All organisms, from humans to amoebas, begin as a single cell. The amoeba and other single-cell organisms remain as single cells, but the original single cell of complex organisms gives rise to thousands of billions of cells that develop along different plans and become specialized as muscle cells, nerve cells, blood cells, and so on. When a cell divides, each new cell from the division is provided with the same kind and amount of genetic information in the form of DNA. And so various kinds of cells are able to produce more cells like themselves.

Although plant and bacterial cells follow most of the rules of animal cells, they differ by having a protective tough cell wall just outside the cell membrane sac. Plant cells also have a special group of organelles that animal cells lack. Called chloroplasts, they contain the green matter chlorophyll that is needed for green plants to manufacture the sugar food glucose, which plants and animals alike depend on as a source of energy and nutrients. The process by which green plants manufacture their glucose is called photosynthesis.

There are two main classes of cells: PROKARYOTES include bacteria and blue-green algae; both are single-cell organisms that lack a nucleus and lack membrane-coated organelles. EUKARYOTES include single-cell and complex plants, animals, and fungi. Cells of this class have a well-defined nucleus, organelles enclosed within membranes, and genetic material organized into structures called chromosomes.

THE VIRUSES: WHAT ARE THEY?

The first organisms on Earth may have been simple structures resembling present-day viruses. There are many hundreds of different kinds of viruses, and all are remarkable and baffling structures. They are not even cells. They cannot move about on their own and are completely inactive until they

One type of virus called a bacteriophage ("bacteria-eater") has a head, protein sheath, and a complex tail. The head contains the genetic material (DNA or RNA) that takes over a host cell and makes the cell produce more viruses instead of more bacteria.

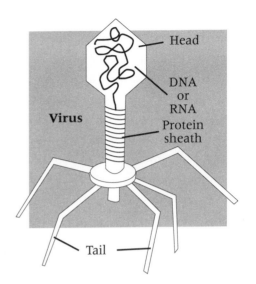

Virus

Head

DNA or RNA

Protein sheath

Tail

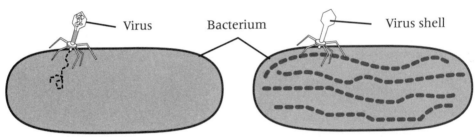

Virus   Bacterium   Virus shell

(1) The virus injects its genetic material into the bacterium.

(2) New viruses begin to form within the bacterium.

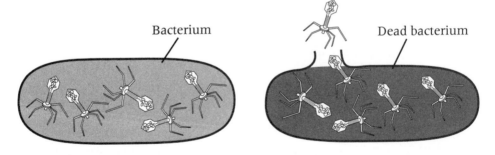

Bacterium   Dead bacterium

(3) New viruses are completely formed.

(4) The new viruses leave the dead bacterial cell and are ready to infect more bacterial cells.

come in contact with a living cell, which they then invade and either destroy or enslave. Although they are made up of two substances present in all organisms, viruses may not be living matter at all. Some are rod-shaped, others sphere-shaped, and still others have distinct segments—a head, sheath, and tail. The two substances of a virus are protein and a nucleic acid, either DNA or RNA.

When a virus quite by chance is pushed into contact with the surface of a living cell, the virus may plunge its hollow tail into the cell, contract its protein sheath, and then inject the DNA or RNA molecule contained in its head into the cell. Within a minute of the time a virus binds itself to a cell's surface, the cell stops making materials that keep it alive and begins to make materials needed by the virus to produce more viruses. Those materials are new virus-protein molecules and new virus-DNA or -RNA molecules. The new molecules are then assembled within the cell into new complete viruses. Within half an hour the cell bursts and spills out its contents of new viruses, each of which now has an opportunity to infect another intact living cell.

Viruses are one of the major agents of disease and illness, causing the common cold, pneumonia, AIDS, yellow fever, smallpox, polio, mumps, German measles, chicken pox, encephalitis, hepatitis, shingles, genital and oral herpes, rabies, and possibly certain types of cancer. They also are the cause of many plant diseases.

THE ORIGIN OF LIFE

SPONTANEOUS GENERATION. The term "spontaneous generation" refers to an old belief that living creatures continually arise fully formed from mixtures of various substances, including mud, water, grains, and so on. Aristotle taught that fleas and mosquitoes were generated spontaneously out of decaying matter and that fireflies arose out of morning dew.

Almost always such beliefs are the result of drawing incorrect conclusions from observation. For example, the ancient Egyptians were convinced that mice were generated spontaneously from mud. This was an incorrect conclusion based on the correct observation that sudden plagues of mice occurred each year after the Nile flooded its banks. Silt carried down by the flood waters was thought to be the matter out of which the mice were "created spontaneously." Actually the mice had been flooded out of their nests and were seeking drier places.

The problem of spontaneous generation was put to rest in the 1800s by the French scientist Louis Pasteur. He experimented with many different kinds of microscopic organisms and showed that (1) a long enough boiling time will kill all such organisms in milk, wine, water, meat broth, and other substances; and (2) on exposure to the air, all such substances become infected with bacteria. Pasteur's experiments showed beyond a doubt that "germs" do not arise spontaneously in such substances.

In one experiment, Pasteur made a glass flask with a long neck that narrowed to an opening about the size of a pinhole. Milk, beef broth, or any other purified substance put into these flasks remained pure even though air could enter the flask through the fine opening. Why? Because when bacteria in the air drifted in through the tiny opening they stuck to the side of the glass tubing and remained there. But when Pasteur tilted the flask until some of the liquid ran down and sloshed around near the end and then allowed the liquid to run back into the main part of the flask, the bacteria washed back with the liquid soon multiplied and formed a thriving colony. Pasteur's experiments represent one of the most important triumphs of reason over superstition. Out of them grew the notion of biogenesis—"life comes only from other life."

CHEMICAL EVOLUTION OF LIFE. In an attempt to find out how life began on Earth, scientists turn back the geological clock to about 3.5 billion years ago when the planet was only a billion years old. At that time the atmosphere was different from today's air; almost entirely lacking was the life-sustaining gas oxygen, which was to be added much later.

For the origin of life in that distant geological past, biologists look to ancient, warm, shallow seas and an atmosphere of carbon dioxide, carbon monoxide, methane, ammonia, nitrogen, argon, neon, and certain other gases. There was abundant energy to drive chemical reactions in those warm seas and in that primitive atmosphere: lightning, ultraviolet energy from the Sun, and radioactive energy from the rocks.

In the early 1950s, Stanley Miller, a graduate student at the University of Chicago, designed an experiment to find out just what kinds of life-important molecules might have been built before life arose on Earth. Through a closed system of glass tubing Miller circulated a mixture of hydrogen, methane, ammonia, and water vapor and then bombarded the gases with lightning (spark) discharges for a week. The water vapor condensed as "rain," and the other gases dissolved in the water. When Miller drew off some of the solution and examined it, he found that a number of complex molecules had been formed, molecules that are needed by all living things. Among them were amino acids, which are the building blocks of proteins. Since then other researchers have repeated Miller's experiment and have produced all of the simple building blocks of the complex molecules of living cells.

The amino acids, proteinlike substances, and other complex molecules that were formed naturally early in Earth's history were a far cry from living matter. But over a few hundred million years those molecules seem to have followed courses of chemical evolution that brought them ever closer to becoming living matter.

The next stage in chemical evolution might have been the grouping of certain complex molecules within a protective, porous, bubble-membrane. Those molecules would have included amino acids, simple sugars, and molecules containing phosphate. According to the biologist Lynn Margulis, these first bubble-membranes might have stretched enough to break in two, each half reenclosing and protecting its cargo of organized molecules. Later, she says, molecules within these bubble-membranes may have begun to maintain the membranes. These lifeless cells might have remained active until they used up the energy and the building-supply molecules available to them. After that, their activity would have stopped.

The next step was for "smarter" *protocells* (nonliving cells) to make their own food rather than depend on an outside source of ready-made food.

Biologists suspect that these advanced protocells took in very simple nutrient molecules from the outside environment and combined them into usable "food." Simple raw-material nutrient molecules would have been in greater supply than the more complex ready-made ones. Such advanced protocells would have had an obvious edge over their simpler competitors. Examples of such organisms today are the many different kinds of green plants that take in the raw materials carbon dioxide and water vapor from the air and fashion them into the universal food glucose, a sugar.

During this period of some 200 million years of chemical evolution, if this scenario is correct, protocells acquired another important feature—the ability to make other protocells exactly like themselves. The key to this ability was a complex giant molecule called RNA (*R*ibo-*N*ucleic-*A*cid) that became a part of protocells. RNA formed in those countless small, shallow seas and became enclosed within bubble-membranes. RNA had the ability to select from the chemical environment certain amino acids and other chemical building blocks (nucleotides) and assemble them into protein molecules. Those protein molecules could then start the process of making more RNA. In this way RNA could assemble amino acids into proteins and produce more giant molecules exactly like itself. So at one stage RNA and proteins could have been two chief features of protocells. The RNA was the control center, and the protein molecules served as food and building materials.

During this same period, but probably after the formation of RNA, another important giant molecule evolved—DNA (*D*eoxyribo-*N*ucleic-*A*cid). Think of RNA as a "doer" and DNA as the master "planner." DNA contains the instructions that tell RNA what kind of protein to make. Every living cell of every known organism on Earth has both DNA and RNA. That fact points to a common origin for all living things on Earth, despite life's broad diversity. The particular kind of protein that DNA instructs RNA to make determines that you are you and not an eagle or an elm tree.

All organisms that have been studied are made of protein molecules assembled from only about twenty different amino acids. The amino acids are joined as chains of a few to several hundred amino acid links. And those vital links, the very common denominator of all living things, are made not only by your body—they can be made in a test tube and have been found in meteorites from outer space!

In the 1970s scientists proposed the "life cloud" theory. It suggests that molecules present in dust clouds in space react and form nucleic acids and other molecules that might have reached Earth several billion years ago, beginning the process of chemical evolution that eventually gave rise to the first living cells. Whether that actually happened is not at all certain.

THE FIRST LIVING CELLS. The commonality of DNA and protein that links all life on Earth is our best evidence that the ancestors of life can be traced back nearly four billion years. Sometime around 3.5 billion years ago, membranes enclosing some watery fluid, a collection of protein molecules, RNA, and DNA evolved as the first living cells—organisms that are now called bacteria and are found by the trillions virtually everywhere. They drift about in the air ready to infect us with disease; they live in soil and make it fertile; they live in lake-bottom ooze without oxygen; they break down organic and inorganic matter into its constituent minerals and elements; and they live on and in our bodies where they help digest our food, rid us of wastes, and manufacture vitamin K for our use.

The ability of bacteria to reproduce is astonishing. Each bacterium simply divides in two. Where there was one bacterium, twenty minutes later the one has divided and become two. The two are identical because they have the same kind of DNA and RNA. The two then divide to produce four, and so on. In just one day a single bacterium can give rise to one million others like itself!

We have fossil evidence that bacterial cells existed around 3.5 billion years ago. Once established, those inventive sacs of DNA, RNA, and protein reproduced at an astonishing rate. They were without enemies and had a limitless supply of energy and food—it seems clear that the evolution of living matter on Earth began at least 3.5 billion years ago.

The gap between the most complex molecules of life and the first living cells is enormous. But year by year biologists manage to narrow that gap.

Eventually it is bound to be closed, at which time a blueprint detailing the major steps from chemical evolution of complex molecules of life to the first living cells will be revealed.

MOLECULES OF LIFE

Contained within and orchestrated by our cells, the molecules of life are many and varied, and they function in infinite ways that keep us alive.

CARBOHYDRATES occur in both animals and plants and play two major roles: (1) they are the building-block raw materials of cells; and (2) they are energy-rich molecules, the food and fuel that help cells function. Carbohydrates are the most abundant and least expensive food source. They include rice and potatoes in the form of starch, and fruits and sugar beets in the form of sugar. Carbohydrate molecules are made up of three elements: carbon (C), hydrogen (H), and oxygen (O). In animals, carbohydrates occur as sugars stored as a substance called glycogen. In plants, carbohydrates are stored as starch and cellulose. Cellulose is the substance that makes the cell walls of plants rigid. In both plants and animals carbohydrates move from cell to cell in the form of the sugar glucose. Glucose is the simplest carbohydrate produced by green plants during photosynthesis. All living things depend on glucose as a source of energy.

FATS, including the fat in meat, butter, and cooking oils, are the chief form of stored energy in our bodies. Ounce for ounce, fats store twice as much energy as carbohydrates or proteins. Fats are composed of two chemical units—glycerol and fatty acids. "Saturated" fats are tightly packed, tend to be solid or semisolid, and are typical of animal fats. "Unsaturated" fats are fluid; linseed oil and corn oil are examples.

STEROIDS are related to fats and include vitamin D, adrenalin, and other hormones. Hormones are chemical messengers that are released into the blood by glands to regulate cell function throughout the body. Cholesterol is an important steroid and is part of most cell membranes. Abundant in milk, butter, and eggs, cholesterol is converted into sex hormones. It also can be deposited in the heart's major artery, raising one's risk of a heart attack.

PROTEINS are giant molecules that contain tens of thousands of atoms. Proteins make up cell organelles, cell membranes, blood, and chromosomes. In addition to serving as building blocks of living matter, proteins prepare cells for division and help regulate body chemistry. For example, insulin is a protein hormone that regulates the amount of sugar reaching body tissues through the blood. Because diabetics do not produce enough insulin to regulate their blood sugar levels, they must inject insulin into their bodies. Proteins are composed of units called amino acids. Although there are only twenty different kinds of amino acids that make up proteins, those twenty kinds can be arranged like letters of the alphabet to form a nearly infinite number of protein "words." Because there are millions of different kinds of proteins, no two living organisms (except identical twins) have precisely the same protein makeup.

NUCLEOTIDES are important molecules that serve as: (1) energy carriers in our bodies, (2) coenzymes, and (3) agents involving heredity.

As energy carriers, nucleotide molecules within a cell store energy and release that energy as it is needed to drive a cell's endless chemical reactions involved in growth and maintenance. The most energy-rich nucleotide molecule is one called adenosine triphosphate (ATP).

As coenzymes, nucleotide molecules are carrier molecules that attach (bond) themselves to certain other kinds of molecules and assist enzymes. Enzymes are protein molecules that speed up chemical reactions but do not become part of the chemical reaction, somewhat like a cheerleader speeding up the home team but not playing in the game itself. Coenzymes work with enzymes, like an assistant cheerleader.

As agents involving heredity, nucleotides link together in chain fashion as molecules of nucleic acids—DNA and RNA. Both of these molecules are composed of links of thousands of individual nucleotides. They are carriers of genetic information that determine whether an organism is to be a rice plant or a rhinoceros, or whether a cell is to be specialized for storage of materials or for reproduction.

HEREDITY: WHO WE ARE

Heredity is the transmission of traits from parents to offspring. Traits include features such as tallness, hair and skin color, color blindness, and coordination. We inherit such traits from our parents and their parents through chemical units called genes and chromosomes.

Genes are chemical units that cluster by the thousands along complex molecular threads called chromosomes, or DNA. Chromosomes and their genes are located in the nucleus of each cell. When an ordinary body cell divides and produces two new cells, each new cell receives half of the parent cell's genetic material. As a result, the two new cells are identical.

In human beings, and in other organisms that reproduce by sexual reproduction, inheritance is more complicated. It must be, since no child is identical to either of its parents. Normal males and females have twenty-two pairs of chromosomes called autosomes. In addition, females have an extra pair of sex chromosomes that are labeled XX. Males also have a pair of sex chromosomes, but only one is an X; the other is a smaller Y chromosome.

During the formation of an egg cell in females, the paired chromosomes split so that an egg cell receives twenty-two single autosomes plus one X sex chromosome. During the formation of sperm cells in males, the paired chromosomes also split so that each sperm cell contains twenty-two single autosomes plus an X sex chromosome, just as in the female's egg cell. But a second sperm cell is produced. It also has twenty-two single autosomes, but unlike its companion sperm it carries the male-determining Y chromosome. A human female produces only one egg at a time; a male produces millions of sperm cells—half have an X sex chromosome and half have a Y sex chromosome.

When a female egg cell and a male sperm cell join during fertilization, the egg cell has a 50 percent chance of receiving either a male X sex chromosome OR a Y sex chromosome. Consequently, there are just about as many males as females in the world, females being sexually identified as XX and males as XY.

The autosomes have nothing to do with sex, but they determine hair and eye color and other such traits. Some traits are said to be dominant, or overpowering. Others are recessive and are overpowered. For example:

DOMINANT TRAIT	RECESSIVE TRAIT
Dark skin	White skin
Dark hair	Blond hair
Curly hair	Straight hair
Brown eyes	Blue eyes
Long eyelashes	Short eyelashes

Sex chromosomes can determine characteristics other than gender. For instance, the genetic makeup for color blindness is carried on the sex chromosomes, not the autosomes. All such traits carried by the sex chromosomes are said to be "sex-linked."

When an egg cell and a sperm cell join in fertilization, they give rise to a new individual with one complete set of paired genetic information—half from each parent. That is why the new individual is not identical to either parent but inherits traits from both. But the new individual always has certain traits that neither parent had. How can that be so, and where do those traits come from?

MUTATIONS

If something did not "go wrong" with genes from time to time, life would be dull. There would be far fewer differences, or variation, among people or among roses. Genes can "go wrong" in many different ways to cause variation.

The DNA molecules that make up chromosomes are composed of nucleotides arranged in a certain sequence. A particular number and sequence of nucleotides define a specific gene (for hair color, tallness, and so on). If that gene is changed by having the sequence of its nucleotides changed, we say that a mutation has taken place. Mutations can occur when a cell divides and its DNA molecule duplicates itself. As the molecule splits to form two new DNA molecules, one or more nucleotide units might be omitted in one of the newly formed DNAs. Or two nucleotide units might reassemble out of order. Or a part of a chromosome might break off and be lost as the cell prepares to divide and the DNA strand unravels. Or a chromosome segment—representing a large number of genes—might be lost completely. (The last example is the most serious kind of mutation and can result in death.)

All of these mutations occur naturally. However, they can be speeded up by certain agents: X rays in the doctor's office, certain chemicals we dump into the environment, and radiation from dumps containing wastes from nuclear and atomic weapons plants. Such agents that speed mutations are called mutagens.

Most mutations are harmful, many are crippling, and some are deadly. For example: Women with Turner's syndrome have only one X chromosome instead of the normal XX pair. Such women lack ovaries, are abnormally short, and are mentally retarded. A condition called Klinefelter's syndrome involves males who are XXY; that is, they have an extra X chromosome. They have underdeveloped testes, enlarged breasts, long limbs, and possible mental retardation and sterility. Men with Klinefelter's syndrome tend to be born of older mothers. It appears that with increasing age the eggs produced by women degenerate and so produce abnormalities. Down syndrome occurs in individuals born with an extra chromosome number 21 instead of the normal pair. (Chromosome pairs are numbered.) Such individuals are short, mentally retarded, and relatively short-lived. Down syndrome infants have normal parents, although they tend to be born to older mothers. The condition cannot be passed on from parent to offspring because the individuals rarely live to adulthood and if so, are usually incapable of reproducing.

Because mutations rarely turn out to be advantageous—although some are—they tend not to be common in a population. There are numerous other genetic disorders, some of which are correctable through the new science of genetic engineering.

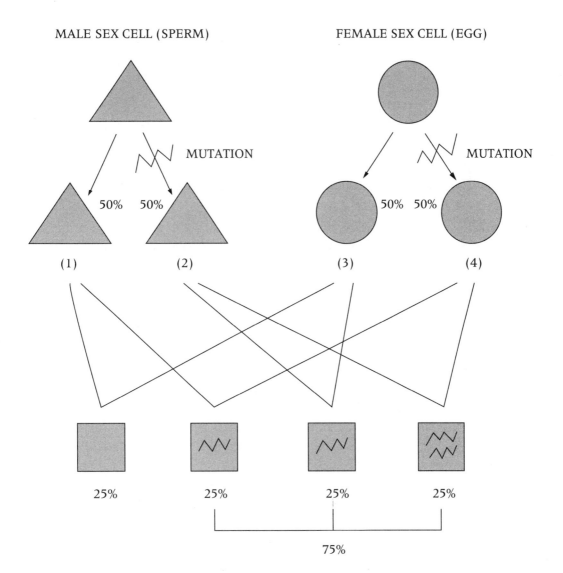

MALE SEX CELL (SPERM)   FEMALE SEX CELL (EGG)

MUTATION   MUTATION

50%   50%   50%   50%

(1)   (2)   (3)   (4)

25%   25%   25%   25%

75%

How mutations in the sex cells (gametes) of a male and female parent can be passed on to their children: If a normal sperm cell (1) fertilizes a normal egg cell (3), the child receives no new genes, only those of its parents. However, if a normal sperm cell (1) fertilizes a mutant egg cell (4), the child receives one new gene from its mother. If a mutant sperm cell (2) fertilizes a normal egg cell (3), the child also receives one new gene, this time from its father. But if a mutant sperm cell (2) fertilizes a mutant egg cell (4), the child receives two new genes, one each from the father and mother. Because about 50 percent of all gametes have one new gene through mutation, 75 percent of offspring have new genes.

VARIATION: WHY YOU'RE YOU

Although you resemble your mother or father in certain ways, you are different in many other ways. Those differences are called variations. They result from genetic "mistakes" made when a strand of DNA from the mother's egg cell combines with the strand of DNA from the father's sperm cell to produce Baby Suzie.

The two DNA strands wrap around each other, separate, and then recombine as Suzie DNA. During the separation the strands swap certain individual genes and groups of genes, which gives rise to certain segments of Suzie's DNA that are different from the DNA strands of either of her parents. In other words, certain of Suzie's parents' genes have been reshuffled and have given Suzie certain traits that neither her mother nor her father has. In addition to mutations, this reshuffling of genes during DNA copying in sex cells—called recombination—is the most important cause of variation. Because a new individual develops from its parents' sex cells (egg and sperm), not from the body cells, only the gene mutations and recombinations of the sex cells can be passed on from parent to offspring.

Biologists think that perhaps 50 percent of all sex cells produced by a person have at least one new mutated gene. Those mutations are the raw materials of the many differences among your friends and among all the individuals in any population of people, dogs, cows, or other organisms that reproduce sexually. It is the changing patterns of variation in a population that provide the driving force of evolution.

HOW ORGANISMS REPRODUCE

Organisms reproduce in one of two ways: In *asexual* reproduction, a new individual is produced by one parent only and, therefore, has only a single set of genes. In *sexual* reproduction, a new individual is produced by the union of a female sex cell with a male sex cell. Because each sex cell contributes one set of genes, the new individual has genes supplied by both parents.

ASEXUAL REPRODUCTION. An amoeba and other single-cell organisms reproduce by a process called division, or binary fission. The cell divides itself into two new "daughter cells," each containing exactly the same genetic material as the one parent.

If you cut a flatworm in two across its middle, the tail portion grows a new head, and the head portion grows a new tail. If you chop a starfish up into several pieces, some may grow, or regenerate, a completely new starfish. These are examples of asexual (meaning nonsexual) reproduction.

Budding is another method of asexual reproduction. In the small fresh-

Like certain other organisms, the small freshwater organism *Hydra* reproduces asexually by growing small buds on its trunk. The buds mature and break off to become new and independent organisms.

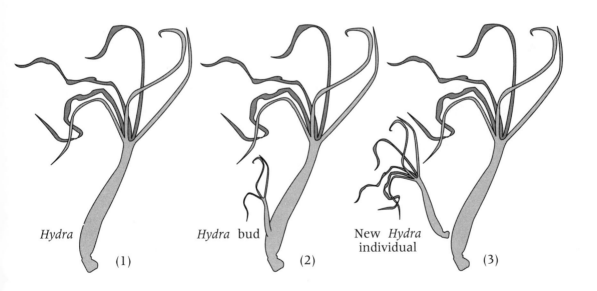

Hydra
(1)

Hydra bud
(2)

New *Hydra* individual
(3)

water organism known as *Hydra*, a tiny twiglike bud forms on the organism's trunk. The bud grows and develops into a new miniature *Hydra* that breaks off and swims away as a new individual. A new plant can also reproduce by asexual reproduction. For example, strawberry plants grow buds that become runners. If a part of several kinds of house plants is cut away and planted, the cut part can develop new root cells and continue life as a complete plant. The new plant grows as a result of vegetative reproduction.

Plant breeders of both flowers and food crop plants have learned to select certain individuals for their beauty of blossom, hardiness, resistance to disease or drought, quality of edible parts, and other traits. The desirable plants are then bred true, meaning that "foreign" genes are kept out of their reproductive systems. All may be well for a time, but an insect pest or certain disease against which the pure-bred plant has no genetic protection may claim an entire crop, or an entire species. For example, in the 1970s the citrus fruit known as jeruk Bali was wiped out in Indonesia by a killer virus. Such calamities tend to occur when breeders continuously undermine the genetic variation of a plant. A solution to the problem of gene-poor food plants is to crossbreed them with wild-type plants in order to increase their natural defenses through gene enrichment. Farmers in many parts of the world have long known the value of fighting pests and plant diseases, and overcoming the limitations of poor soils and unfavorable weather conditions by breeding several different genetic varieties of a crop.

Many plants and animals reproduce by asexual reproduction, but some of those same plants and animals can also reproduce by sexual reproduction. Sexual reproduction has many important advantages over asexual reproduction.

SEXUAL REPRODUCTION involves the union of genetic material carried by sex cells (gametes) from a male parent and a female parent. In females, the genetic material is carried in egg cells; in males it is carried in sperm cells. During fertilization, or the union of an egg cell with a sperm cell, the genetic material of both parents is combined in the new individual. One important advantage of sexual reproduction over asexual reproduction is the infinite number of possibilities for new gene combinations, which result in variation.

In plants and animals that reproduce by sexual reproduction, no two gametes of a population (or of a given individual) have *exactly* the same collection of genes. In addition, mating is a rather random process. Consequently, there is a good deal of chance involved in the combination of genes during fertilization, and that is the driving force of variation in a population of tulips, turtles, or tigers. For example, some fish release their eggs and sperm directly into the water at spawning time. Which sperm fertilize which eggs is left almost entirely to chance.

The variation that results from random mating usually is critical to the health of a population. Environmental change can cause many individuals to die. That is, individuals lacking the "right" genes to tolerate an environmental change will die; other individuals with the "right" genes will tolerate the change in environmental conditions and thrive. They will then pass their "survival genes" on to their offspring, who also can thrive in the new conditions. The latter individuals are selected for by nature. Selection pressure by nature according to an individual's genetic makeup is called natural selection, and it is the driving force of evolution.

EVOLUTION AND HOW IT WORKS

All organisms of a single kind, such as dogs, cats, white birch trees, or people, are said to belong to a certain species. Human beings, for instance, belong to the species *Homo sapiens*, and cats belong to the species *Felis domesticus*. We can define a species as a population of individuals that generally look pretty much alike and can produce offspring that can in turn produce offspring.

All known organisms, despite their marked differences, have many, pronounced similarities, and they have evolved from common ancestors over thousands of millions of years.

Over long periods of time a species may change, or evolve, into a new species. Or all members of a species may die, in which case the species becomes extinct, which is what happened to the many species of dinosaurs some sixty-five million years ago. Of all the species of animals and plants that have ever lived on Earth, 99.99 percent are now extinct. However, life itself has gone on uninterrupted as new species have evolved and repopulated Earth.

Sometimes extinctions occur quietly and go unnoticed. Other times they are catastrophic. Several single catastrophic events have shaken Earth in the past, each wiping out most of all living species. Biologists generally agree that the largest wholesale extinction of species is now taking place. Its cause: Overpopulation of the human species is causing increased degradation of the environment.

When scientists study the ways in which living matter has evolved since it first appeared on Earth nearly four billion years ago, they examine life on many different levels—the level of cells, the level of whole organisms, the level of populations of those organisms, and the level of communities of different kinds and populations of organisms.

With the Sun as a source of energy, nonliving matter on at least one planet (Earth) was organized into the simplest bacterialike living matter in a process of chemical evolution about 3.8 billion years ago. Over the following thousands of millions of years, that first living matter underwent a long process of biological change that gave rise to all the complex life forms known to us today and in fossil history.

The evolution that has occurred on Earth needs a lot of time, a continuous source of energy to keep things neither too hot nor too cold, and a favorable and ever-changing environment. A population's ability to be in tune with its environment at a given time and to adjust, or adapt, to changes in the environment depends on the genetic variation among the individuals making up the population. Variation, in turn, depends on mutation. Variation among individuals expresses itself in many ways—an animal's strength when forced to fight, the warmth its fur provides, the biochemistry of its hormones and digestive enzymes. Some individuals are better at finding food during hard times; others are better at withstanding the heat; some are swifter in escaping predators or catching prey; others are smarter at solving problems, and so on.

If the climate turns cold, individuals who can withstand the cold because of an insulating coat of fur or a more efficient body chemistry survive; those who can't withstand the cold die. The survivors mate and pass their "cold-survival" genes on to their offspring and into the population's total collection of genes (the gene pool). Gradually the population changes as the less fit individuals are weeded out by natural selection and the more fit individuals survive. The more fit individuals are the ones who, by reproducing, keep adding their genes to the population's gene pool. Through the process of beneficial change in the gene pool, a population adapts to changes in its environment. Change in the gene pool of a population, and the buildup of beneficial genes, is evolution through natural selection; it happens on the level of populations, not on the level of individuals.

Evolution does not give a wolf the ability to change into a dog or allow an ape to change into a human being. Instead, it provides a gradual change in a population, usually over millions of years, and results from environmental change that favors certain variations.

Evolution accounts for similarities in anatomy and molecular chemistry among species, and it also accounts, through natural selection, for diversity among species. Although there are thousands of spoken languages, there is only one genetic language: the language of the interchangeable components of DNA. The way in which DNA is duplicated in kangaroos, caterpillars, and all other species is the same, but the composition of the DNA molecule differs in each species. Therefore, the genetic language of DNA is responsible for the unity of all living organisms and for their marvelous and endless diversity.

Nowhere is diversity more striking than in a tropical rain forest. So many and so varied are the designs and behaviors of a tropical rain forest's plant and animal communities, and so bewildering their infinite interactions, that biologists who study the forests feel overwhelmed. South America's Amazonia has 1,171 known bird species, but there are more. Brazil has 1,383 known fish species, but there are more. Central America has 456 fish species, but there are more. Compare those numbers with the total of 192 fish species in all of Europe and only 172 in the Great Lakes. Species of insects, as well as their individual numbers, are countless. They whir, whine, hum, and buzz with a million different voices.

The result of evolution is not a ladder ranging from the most ''primitive'' organisms on the lower rungs to the most ''advanced'' at the top. Instead it is like a tree. Some branches have died in the course of time, others have remained pretty much the same, and still others have developed additional branches that continually give rise to new species.

The fact that evolution has occurred cannot be refuted on scientific grounds. The evidence of a sequence of changes in fossils found in successive rock layers dating back more than a billion years is overwhelming. Evolution is the unifying principle underlying biology, and Earth's history of life makes no sense without this unifying principle. Evolution occurs all around us, and it responds to the influence of human activity, which year by year nudges natural selection in ways we are just beginning to understand, and in many cases may come to regret.

EVOLUTION AND CREATIONISM.   Does everyone accept evolution as a fact?

Almost all biologists and other scientists are convinced by the fossil record that evolution has occurred throughout the past and that it continues today.

TIMETABLE OF EVOLUTION

Earth formed	First biological cells	Bacterial fossils	Algae	Water plants and animals lacking backbones	Psilopsids become first land plants
4.6 billion years ago	3.8 billion years ago	3.5 billion years ago	2 billion years ago	590 million years ago	430 million years ago

EVOLUTION THROUGH THE AGES

The evolution of life on Earth has proceeded in several broad steps. The first biological cells organized themselves into bacterialike organisms some 3.8 billion years ago. Bacterial fossils 3.5 billions years old have been found in western Australia. Microscopic fossils of algae 2 billion years old have been found on the shore of Lake Superior in Ontario. By 590 million years ago shallow seas abounded with water plants and animals including sponges, trilobites, brachiopods, and others lacking backbones. About 430 million years ago plants called psilopsids were the first to take up life on land. Then about sixteen million years later the first animals—millipedes and scorpionlike creatures—also became established on land.

Fishes branched out into so many species and were so abundant around 380 million years ago that the period is known as the Age of Fishes. Lobe-finned fishes, which were midway between fishes and amphibians, gave rise to true amphibians about 370 million years ago. About 290 million years ago amphibians were so numerous that the period is known as the Age of Amphibians. Reptiles evolved from amphibians and dominated the land during the Age of Reptiles, some 150 million years ago. Dinosaurs were among the reptiles.

By the time the dinosaurs had become extinct, some 65 million years ago, a new group—the mammals—had evolved from the reptiles and were taking command. Mammals continue to rule the land, and among them human beings have evolved to a position of dominance over the past half million or so years. Humans differ from all other animal groups in several important ways, including a complex language and the ability to accumulate experience, which has produced culture. Perhaps humans are best described as a cultural animal.

First land animals	Age of Fishes	First amphibians	Age of Amphibians	Age of Reptiles	Mammals begin to dominate the land
414 million years ago	380 million years ago	370 million years ago	290 million years ago	150 million years ago	65 million years ago

All life forms known to us today and in the past, they say, gradually evolved from earlier and simpler life forms; and those earlier and simpler life forms in turn evolved from natural substances such as amino acids and proteins that formed at the beginning of Earth's history as a planet. Most scientists also trust the many ways they have of dating the age of Earth's rocks and fossils. The evidence shows that Earth has a very long geological history, one that goes back some 4.6 billion years.

But there are many people—some scientists among them—who refuse to accept evolution as a fact. Most of the people who say no to evolution do so on religious grounds. They contend that the Bible should be believed word for word, that everything written in the Bible is true, exactly as it is described. To these people, the Bible is the "word of God." For example, two chapters in the Bible's Book of Genesis state that God created the world and all life in six days. Belief in that biblical description of the creation of the world is called creationism. Creationists, therefore, deny evolution because it contradicts the Bible.

Creationists believe that the world is only about 10,000 years old, not 4.6 billion years old, as scientists maintain. Creationists do not trust the scientific methods of determining the age of rocks and fossils; accordingly they claim that humans and dinosaurs lived side by side and that the last dinosaurs died out only a few thousand years ago, when the first American Indians crossed over to North America from Siberia. But that claim means that the dinosaurs lived during an ice age, and the dinosaurs were reptiles, cold-blooded animals. No scientific evidence or theories can explain how a cold-blooded dinosaur could have existed in the cold climate of a North American ice age. Creationists further believe that scientific views about the origin of the Solar System are wrong, and that their "research" will prove that what the Bible says about the origin of the world and of life is true in every detail. However, the creationists have not yet produced any evidence from their "research."

Not all religious people agree with the creationists. Many accept and use the Bible as a source of spiritual enlightenment and do not insist on its word-for-word "factual" accuracy, as if it were a textbook of science.

SOCIAL ORGANIZATION

There are virtually as many different social systems among species as there are species, although social organization among similar species tends to vary less. Some colonial social systems—as among bees and ants— number from a few hundred to millions of individuals. Through genetic programming, the colony rather than the individual is the "organism." At the other extreme, in many species of mammals individuals are genetically programmed to customarily avoid others except during the mating season. Although certain aspects of human behavior seem to be controlled by our genetic makeup, other aspects of our behavior are molded by our social environment and by our intellectual environment. (The social behavior of human beings is discussed in Chapter 5, "Human Behavior.")

BEES—Social systems among bees are remarkable for their rigid structure. A colony of honeybees, for example, may number several hundred bees, among which are three classes—the queen, female workers, and male drones. The hive is kept orderly by chemical signals (pheromones) given off by the queen. The workers forage for food in response to the dance pattern of workers just returned from the field. The dance informs the other workers about the distance, direction, and richness of the food source. In addition to keeping the hive supplied with food and water, in hot weather the workers beat their wings to fan the hive interior, thus maintaining a constant temperature. Soldier and guard workers fight off would-be hive intruders while nurse workers tend to the larvae.

When a queen grows old and feeble, her regulating pheromones weaken. The workers then prepare developing larvae for queenship. Battle among the rival queens results in the death of all but one, which then flies from the hive to mate with drones who have swarmed and await the queen. With her eggs now fertilized, the queen returns to the hive, lays her eggs, and takes charge. The workers care for the eggs, and by their care determine which of the larvae will develop into more workers, drones, or new queens. In colonial insects, the good of the colony is placed above the good of any individual. Despite the high efficiency of a bee colony, more than 90 percent of bee species are solitary.

FISHES—Many fish species live near the surface where there is no place to hide from predators. Protection in numbers—living in schools—is the rule for such fishes. School fish are remarkable for their precision of group motion and spacing; their best defense is to act in unison, rapidly and suddenly. They do so through sensitivity to visual cues and to sudden changes in water pressure caused by tail motions. Visual cues are easily read because all the males and females have identical body shapes and markings. If males and females were different in their schooling behavior and had different markings, there would be two or more sets of visual cues, and therefore, a greater chance for misinterpreted cues.

The females of such school species discharge their eggs into the ocean currents. Males react to the females and discharge their sperm cells at the same time. Timing is extremely important for egg fertilization. Fertilized eggs hatch into young fish, which must care for themselves from the instant they are born.

In some shallow-water fish species a male-female pair performs courtship "dances" that ensure simultaneous release of eggs and sperm. Each step of the courtship dance sequence triggers the next step until both fish dance in unison, the final step being egg and sperm discharge side by side. In other species courtship behavior involves very complex dance signals by the male, whose color markings are very different from those of the female. The male attracts a female to his nest, where the female lays her eggs; she then departs. The male fertilizes the eggs and cares for the young when they hatch.

In many fish species the female releases several clusters of eggs, and each cluster is fertilized by a different male. Such breeding behavior increases the chances of genetic variation. In other species a male and female form long-term pair bonds. The eggs are fertilized, and after they hatch the male and female take turns guarding the young. Fertilization in some species, including guppies, takes place inside the female's body, and there is much competition among males to inseminate females. As in bees and other animal species, each fish species has evolved a mating social system that works successfully in the species' particular habitat.

BIRDS—Most bird species form social groups, called flocks, when they are not breeding. Some flocks contain only birds of the same species; others, such as tropical forest birds, contain several different species. The only birds that do not form flocks are owls, hawks, and other carnivorous (meat-eating) birds.

In most bird species an individual male and female form a mating-pair bond. Usually the male marks out his territory and defends it by vigorous "song" against intrusion by other males. The "song" also serves to attract females. The two then perform courtship displays, such as strutting, neck stretching, wing motions, and so on. Next they build a nest, the male inseminates the female, and the female lays her fertilized eggs. The hatchlings are protected and fed by one or both parents until the young birds learn to fly and leave the nest.

Instead of mating in a territory maintained by a single pair, some birds mate in dense colonies, after which each pair establishes a small territory within the colony. Sea birds such as gulls and penguins form this type of social group. Some colonial nesters form seasonal pair bonds; among others the male visits the nests of several females, mates with them, and drives away competitor males. In other cases the males build and maintain a nest and attract several females to it. Each female is inseminated, lays her eggs, and leaves. The male then cares for all the eggs in his charge and later cares for the hatchlings.

The tropics have several species of cuckoos that build communal nests containing many individuals of both sexes. After the females lay their fertilized eggs, males, females, and juvenile birds alike vie for the "privilege" of incubating the eggs and feeding the hatchlings. This process is regulated by a bird entering the nest with a small green leaf in its beak. The leaf serves as a signal (or "ticket") for the bird presently sitting on the eggs to yield its position to the leafbearer.

In still other species, including cowbirds, females lay their eggs in the nests of other species of birds.

Most bird species have social systems in which a male and female form a mating-pair bond and defend a territory against intruders. Within such species, both birds are alike in appearance rather than the male being the more brightly colored. After the hatchlings have become independent, the male and female parents join a flock and dissolve their pair bond.

MAMMALS—Why do we see so few mammals in the wild? Because most are secretive, small, and active by night rather than by day. Mammals tend to form individual territories and defend them by vocalizations or by marking them with urine, excrement, or highly odorous secretions from glands near the eye. The social rule among most mammals is solitary behavior, except during the mating season.

At breeding time males leave their individual territory, enter the territory of a female, mate with her, and then leave. Each male tries to mate with as many females as possible. The male does not help raise the young, instead the female has an exclusive role in feeding her offspring—all female mammals have special milk-producing glands.

Some mammal species, such as caribou, elk, and certain other hoofed mammals, form all-male or all-female groups between breeding seasons. Some live in unisex herds except during the mating season, at which time one male may protect and mate with his harem of females. Seals and their relatives live in harems during the breeding season but in mixed-sex groups during the non-breeding season.

Some mammals form either permanent harems or all-male groups, all year around; bats, camels, and Hamadryas baboons are examples. Others, such as beavers and gibbons, live in family social units of two parents and their offspring. (Few mammals live in permanent family units.) In other instances several males and several females live in small communities with their collective offspring. Wolves and rabbits are among such groups, in which one or two dominant males do most of the mating.

Why are most mammals solitary creatures? Because most mammals are small, and most small mammals have limited mobility. Their relatively small territory rarely can supply enough food for more than one individual.

Three

UNDERSTANDING THE ENVIRONMENT

THE ENVIRONMENT'S MAJOR PARTS

If someone put you in the middle of a large field and left you with instructions to write a report on it, where would you begin? One way would be to count how many different kinds of plants you could identify. Another would be to distinguish between those plants that grow in a low and wet part of the field and those that grow at higher and drier elevations. You could then catalog all the organisms living in the field. Or you could describe the climate, soil, and other nonliving parts of the field. Or you could study the interrelationships of all the animal species or of all of the plant species, or the interaction of plants and animals within the field.

For instance, a hummingbird feeds on the nectar of flowers and, as a result, pollinates the flowers. Mice and sparrows can then eat the seeds produced by these flowers and spread them far and near. The flowers depend on both hummingbirds and mice for their continued success, and the hummingbirds and mice depend on the flowers for their continued success. Such possibilities of study are nearly endless and gradually lead to an understanding of the field.

Such investigations as those would be a first step in ordering the environment into categories. Ecologists, scientists who study the environment, similarly order the environment into various categories for ease of studying it and feeling at home in it. The more we know about our surroundings— our house, a city block, or a small patch of forest—the more we feel at home, and our sense of belonging to and caring about our surroundings grows.

A field is an ecological system, or an ecosystem, consisting of many living and nonliving parts. An even larger ecological unit is a biome, which consists of collections of different ecosystems. We can speak of a desert biome, or a north coniferous forest biome, a mid-latitude deciduous forest biome, a tropical rain forest biome, and so on.

Within every biome there are populations of plants and animals. We can describe a population as a group of organisms that closely resemble each other and live, mate, and produce offspring, which means that they all belong to the same species. There are populations of seals, of tulips, and of earthworms.

The term "community" refers to an ecological unit that is smaller than a biome. A community is made up of all the populations of an area, such as a field, a small pond, or a saltwater marsh. Ecologists may study the entire community, or they may restrict their study to smaller parts of it—the small mammals, for instance, or the foliage-insects.

An ecosystem includes all of the plant and animal populations of a community plus the physical environment itself. So an ecosystem has two parts—the living (biotic) part and the nonliving (abiotic) part. Likewise, the still larger unit, the ecosphere, also has two parts—the living (biosphere) part and the nonliving part. We can think of the ecosphere as an ecosystem on a global scale. At the other extreme, the smallest ecological unit is called a habitat, the place where an organism lives. An old-growth forest with lots of dead and hollow trees is the habitat of the Pacific Northwest's spotted owl. A stream is the habitat of the larval stages of Maine's pesky black flies.

Ecologists use the term "niche" to describe an organism's occupation, or role, in its habitat or in its community; what the organism does and what is done to it. In the broadest sense, ecologists are most interested in the roles populations—including human populations—play as active living units of the environment.

And finally, the environment can be broken down into such categories as water, air, temperature, amount of light, dissolved salts, and the availability of elements such as oxygen, nitrogen, sulfur, sodium, calcium, and phosphorus.

As we learn about the environment, we begin to ask how this or that organism is adapted to making its particular kind of living in its habitat or community. We then learn to appreciate how its activities affect other species in the habitat or community. Ultimately we are able to evaluate the *function* of this or that species in the environment.

According to biologist Mary Clark of San Diego State University, "modern industrial society has tended to estrange itself from the natural world, treating it as something alien—to be shunned, tamed, or exploited. Before we can adjust the human behaviors that now threaten the planet, we have to adjust our attitudes toward the planet, and doing so requires a friendly familiarity with the ways in which it functions."

PRODUCERS, CONSUMERS, AND DECOMPOSERS

We live in a spaceship called planet Earth. Like the starship *Enterprise*, spaceship Earth is traveling among the stars as it is carried around our home galaxy by the motion of the Sun. Also like the *Enterprise*, spaceship Earth is a closed ecological system, as were the Apollo craft sent to the Moon and the space shuttle when in orbit high above Earth.

Energy from the Sun drives a number of chemical reactions that produce the food we eat and recycle the wastes generated at all levels within the environment. Those wastes ultimately are converted back into materials that are reused over and over again. The ecological system of spaceship Earth is "closed" because new materials (except for meteorites) are not imported from space and waste materials are not exported into space.

Energy production in the biosphere depends on radiant energy from the Sun and begins with green plants. Green plants are called producers because they use the Sun's radiant energy to convert carbon dioxide and water into chemical energy, which they store as carbohydrate. When consumers eat

A typical terrestrial food chain consists of producers, (grass and shrubs, for instance), herbivores such as deer, primary carnivores such as mountain lions, secondary carnivores such as humans, and finally the decomposers of the soil.

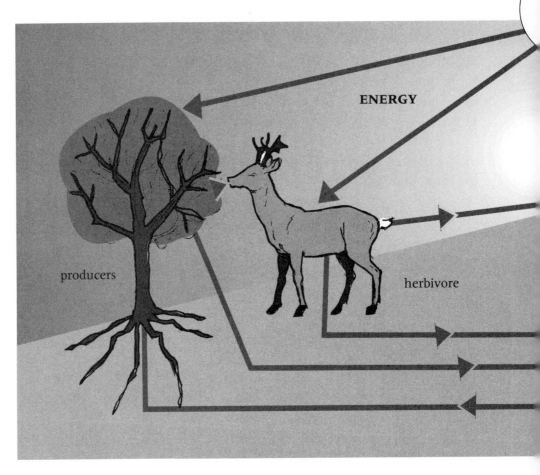

green plants, they convert that stored chemical energy into mechanical energy. The consumers produce organic wastes, and themselves become organic wastes when they die. Finally, their remains, as well as those of plants, are broken down by the decomposers—fungi and bacteria—and recycled as molecules and atoms that can be used once again by living organisms. The following sections explain in detail how this chain of energy capture and transfer works.

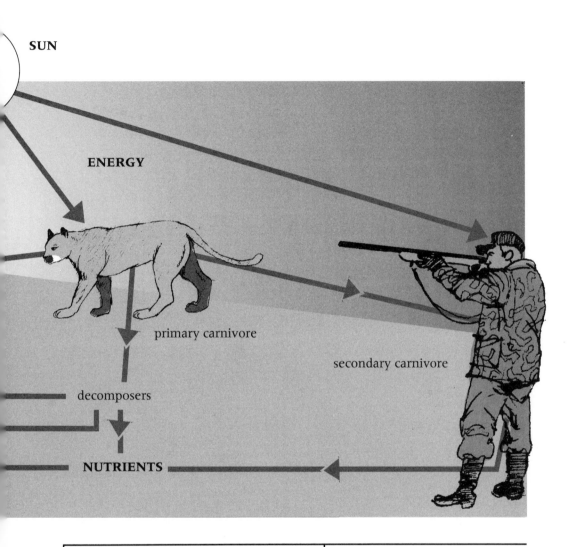

SUN

ENERGY

primary carnivore

secondary carnivore

decomposers

NUTRIENTS

PHOTOSYNTHESIS AND RESPIRATION

During the day, green plants—grasses, shrubs, and trees—carry on a remarkable chemical transformation called photosynthesis. With the aid of tiny green structures (chloroplasts) inside the leaves, water and carbon dioxide from the air are combined by the radiant energy of sunlight. In the process, the leaves give off free oxygen to the air. The chemical reaction of photosynthesis also produces the carbohydrate glucose, a sugar that is used to nourish the plant. Green plants (and certain bacteria able to carry on photosynthesis) also store some of the glucose as starch, which can be called upon by the plant for future energy needs.

$$CO_2 \quad + \quad H_2O \quad \rightarrow \quad [CH_2O] \quad + \quad H_2O \quad + \quad O_2$$

Carbon dioxide	Water vapor	Glucose	Water	Oxygen

The carbohydrate of green plants provides the only source of nourishment for animals called herbivores—cows, horses, and deer, for example. As a rule, cows do not eat hamburgers, although I once knew of a horse that ate hotdogs. These animals are taking in from the environment the carbohydrate they cannot produce for themselves. Without green plants they would die, and so would all other animals that depend on green plants or depend on the animals that depend on green plants as a food source; in other words, virtually all living organisms.

In addition to providing the world with carbohydrate, green plants (such as grass, potatoes, and beets, for instance) take up nutrients from the soil, including the mineral elements iron, calcium, potassium, magnesium, and phosphorus and use them to make their proteins and fats. These elements too are passed on to the animals that eat green plants. The carbohydrates, mineral elements, proteins, and fats that we get from green plants and the animals we eat are collectively called food. Our digestive system chemically breaks down the food we eat, providing a source of body-building materials used for growth and the replacement of worn or damaged parts. During the chemical breakdown of food, the energy needed to operate our personal chemical factory, to enable us to run, breathe, and think, is also made available to us. The process of breaking down nutrient molecules of food, and providing energy, is called respiration. The total chemical activity of an organism is called metabolism.

The green leaves of all forest and other plants make carbohydrate during the daylight hours. During the night, when light levels are too low, the photosynthetic machinery of a green plant is shut down. The green plant then must draw on its stored energy, starch, to power its chemical factory.

So we can look on photosynthesis as a means of providing energy for all living things, and on respiration as the process of using that energy for growth and maintenance.

ENERGY FOR ECOSYSTEMS

If there is one central and unifying idea in ecology it is this: Life goes on as a result of the collective ability of Earth's organisms to use the Sun's radiant energy. In a seemingly endless process of death and renewal, the Sun's energy is used to continuously recycle the atoms and molecules that make up living matter.

You are an energy system; so is a carrot, and so is the Earth-Sun association. One important idea about any energy system is that it runs down to zero unless some outside source of energy keeps feeding it. In other words, any energy system, including a walking toy dog driven by a windup spring, has to be kept "wound up." A scientist might put the thought this way: *There is a trend of increasing disorder in the universe.*

The Sun is aging and one day will lose its ability to produce enough radiant energy to drive photosynthesis and other life processes on Earth. At that stage, some 5 billion years from now, Earth will "wind down" and stop, meaning that life on the planet will simply cease because it will have run out of an energy source. Meanwhile, as the Sun keeps shining, life goes on because the planet has an outside source of energy to power its many biological operations.

Although the organic molecules and atoms essential to life can be recycled and used over and over again, energy cannot be recycled; energy flows along a one-way street. It enters an energy system, such as you or a carrot, is used up, and is gone forever. There is nothing left of it to be recaptured and used again. The only way you and the carrot can keep going is to have a continual supply of more and more energy. If energy flows along a one-way street and is eventually used up and reduced to zero, what happens to it along the way to get lost?

FOOD CHAINS

The last hamburger you ate came from a steer that ate green plants as a source of energy. Or, if you prefer salmon, the salmon you ate fed in part on mosquitoes, which fed on the blood of rabbits, which ate the leaves and roots of green plants. (The process always starts with the green-plant producers.) These are examples of food chains and of energy being passed along from one level of organisms—called a trophic level—to the next higher trophic level. The first example above involves a two-link food chain. The second involves a four-link chain.

The green-plant producers are eaten by the plant-eating consumer herbivores (deer, for example), and the herbivores are eaten by the meat-eating primary carnivores (maybe a mountain lion). Primary carnivores may then be eaten by secondary carnivores (humans). Some animals, such as grasshoppers and squirrels, are always herbivores, but others feed at several different trophic levels. Bears are herbivores when they eat berries, but carnivores when they eat a deer.

At the end of all food chains are the decomposers, the bacteria and fungi that feed on and transform the organic remains at all trophic levels to reusable nutrients. A typical food chain on land might be like that shown in the diagram. Energy is transferred from one link to the next along this four-link food chain. But just how much energy gets passed along from one link to the next? In other words, how efficient is energy flow in an ecosystem?

ENERGY FLOW IN ECOSYSTEMS

Only part of the food-energy consumed at each trophic level is used to build new body mass. The rest is used to drive chemical reactions, and some is lost as heat. While much of the stored energy you use when you run enables your muscles to do the work of running, some is lost as the heat that causes you to sweat. That energy can never be regained for reuse, nor can the energy that made your muscles work.

Depending on the species of consumer, as much as 50 to 90 percent of the food eaten passes through the gut unused and is expelled as waste. In cows, about 30 percent of the food digested and used is turned into new body mass. The remaining 70 percent is used to drive all the chemical reactions that keep the cow alive. Carnivores are more efficient than herbivores, using up to 70 percent of the energy they take in and wasting about 30 percent.

The left column of the following chart shows energy loss along a food chain involving algae as producers, then copepod grazers, smelt, trout, and human carnivore consumers. Notice that it takes 100 energy units of algae to produce 15 energy units of copepods, that only three units of smelt result from the 15 energy units of copepods, and so on up to a human consumer. It takes 100 energy units of algae to produce what fraction of an energy unit of a human being in a five-link food chain?

ENERGY TRANSFER		BODY MASS TRANSFER
HUMAN	0.06 energy units	10 ounces
TROUT	0.6 energy units	6 pounds
SMELT	3.0 energy units	30 pounds
COPEPODS	15.0 energy units	150 pounds
ALGAE	100.0 energy units	1,000 pounds

The right column of the chart translates energy units into body mass transfer up the same food chain. In short, it takes 1,000 pounds of algae to produce only 10 ounces of human being along a five-link food chain. One lesson to be learned from this: It would be much more economical for the human at the top of the food chain to eat the algae and end up with 150 pounds of new body mass instead of 10 ounces. As much as we may like hamburgers and steaks, it would be much more energy efficient for us to spare the cattle and eat the grass ourselves rather than eat the steer that eats the grass or corn.

The chart illustrates two major concepts: (1) The shorter the food chain, the more efficiently energy is used and the less the waste. (2) Overall productivity in any ecosystem—meaning energy production and the production of plant or animal mass—is determined by the rate of photosynthesis, which in turn is controlled by a number of factors—e.g. the amount and degree of sunlight and the availability of moisture and nutrients.

In a number of Third World countries where productivity is low, food is so scarce that the people cannot afford to waste the energy lost by turning over a sizeable part of their green-plant producers to animals. They have been forced to eliminate grazing animals from their menus. That situation has become the rule in many world areas where too many people demand from the environment an amount of food that the environment cannot provide.

CARRYING CAPACITY OF THE ENVIRONMENT

Populations of organisms interact with and depend on the health of other populations of organisms with which they share an ecosystem. The well-being of a population also depends on an adequate supply of water, food, and living space, such as grazing land for a herd of elephants or nesting sites for a population of blackbirds. The health of a given population also depends on the degree of competition for any of these things with other populations of the same species, or of different species. And finally, in humans, the quality of life enjoyed by individuals affects the mental and physical health of its various populations. All such aspects of the environment that provide for a population to be stable and healthy are called the carrying capacity of the environment.

If any one or more aspects of the environment's carrying capacity are upset, a population may "crash," meaning that its numbers are greatly reduced by disease or starvation. The population will not recover until its numbers are once again in equilibrium with the environment's carrying capacity. An example will make this clear.

Years ago the prickly-pear cactus was introduced in Australia. It thrived and quickly took over thousands of square miles in Queensland, becoming an unwanted pest. To keep it under control, Australian scientists introduced a Central American moth species whose caterpillar stage feeds on the cactus. Because the moth species had no competition and an abundant food supply, Queensland's carrying capacity for the moth was great. But the moth population grew rapidly, and the caterpillars soon ate most of the cactus. Quite suddenly, Queensland's carrying capacity for the moth seriously decreased, and the moth population crashed. However, as intended, the moth effectively destroyed the pear cactus.

The environment's carrying capacity applies not only to moths and cacti, but to all populations, including human beings. Any population of plants or animals risks crashing when it grows so large that it exceeds one or more aspects of the environment's carrying capacity. In view of the rapid growth of the world's human population today, that principle of nature is a major lesson for all of us to learn and understand.

FEEDING THE WORLD'S PEOPLE

Until about 10,000 years ago there were no cities. People lived in loosely associated groups of families, numbering a few hundred or less. Some lived in temporary villages on a seasonal basis. Most were hunter-gatherers, following the game they depended on for food and gathering seasonal berries, wild fruit, and nuts, as had their ancestors for more than 100,000 years. Others chose a somewhat more settled life in semi-permanent shelters of wood or animal skins, but they were still hunter-gatherers who prospered when game and food plants were plentiful and went hungry when food was scarce.

When times were good and the carrying capacity of the environment permitted, local populations tended to increase. When times were bad, populations held their own or declined. Whether times were good or bad, one of every two infants died during its first year of life from malnutrition, disease, accidents, or neglect. When there were too many mouths to feed, infants were killed and women had abortions so that the population might survive. Ten thousand years ago the world's human population was about 5 million—the present population of Missouri, or of Finland.

Then a revolution occurred, a revolution in food production. People learned to farm, which meant that many more mouths could be fed. And many more were. The carrying capacity of the environment had suddenly skyrocketed due to the new practice of controlled agriculture. In part as a result of the agricultural revolution, by November 1992 the world population was 5.45 *billion*, and it is growing faster than ever before in Earth's history—at the rate of 91 million per year. A question that seriously concerns many ecologists is "How much longer can the human population keep growing at an ever-faster rate before overstepping the carrying capacity of the environment?"

According to World Bank estimates, more than one sixth of the world's population now lives in absolute poverty, barely able to survive. About 500 million people suffer from malnutrition, which is caused by lack of food or by inadequate amounts of one or more essential nutrients, such as protein, calcium, or vitamin C. Further, on a worldwide basis, deaths due to malnutrition of children under age five number about 10 million a year. In India alone a million children die from malnutrition each year. On a global basis 12,000 people die of starvation each day.

In today's world of food production, agriculture and domesticated animals such as cattle and chickens have replaced hunting and gathering. Until the early 1960s, most nations that needed more food opened up new farmlands. Since then, the amount of cropland has grown relatively slowly; using fertilizers, pesticides, and new plant varieties, an effort called the "green revolution" has tried to increase the amount of food that can be produced from a given amount of land. Among the results were new strains of high-yield "miracle rice" and "miracle wheat," crops that at best filled many mouths temporarily while the population continued to grow. The temporary relief came at a terrible cost.

First, high-technology agriculture involves irrigation, and without adequate drainage, which is expensive, extensive irrigation spells trouble. A poorly drained irrigation system causes a buildup of salts in the water bathing the root-zone level of the crops. When too many salts collect, the yield of a crop is reduced, and the crop is eventually destroyed.

High-technology agriculture also uses huge amounts of fertilizers, pesticides, and machinery; the result is more pollution. And in many areas, old storage and transportation systems had to be replaced, at great expense. In 1981 in India, for example, it cost more than 5 billion dollars each year for fertilizers, pesticides, and agricultural equipment to feed that nation's people at a bare self-sufficiency level.

Widespread use of pesticides has posed some especially interesting problems. The pesticides worked well enough for a while, but then many of the insect pests they were supposed to control developed immunity to the poisons through genetic mutations. Humans, however, have not developed immunity, and the World Health Organization of the United Nations estimates that hundreds of thousands of people die each year from acute pesticide poisoning.

Still another problem of the "green revolution" is the risk of putting all our plant genes in one basket. As the many genetically different types of rice and wheat are replaced with only a few genetic varieties, those few varieties are more vulnerable to the many plant diseases and insect pests. For example, in 1946 a new, single oat variety was planted on 30 million acres of U.S. land. The new variety, called "Victoria type," was hailed as being resistant to a plant disease known as rust, but it did not have the genetic mixture of traditional oat seeds. All went well for the first two years. Then a new plant disease struck and wiped out the Victoria type, which had a limited genetic defense; it disappeared almost overnight from those 30 million acres.

The "miracle rice" and "miracle wheat" varieties that were so successful in the 1970s were far less successful in the 1980s as yields dropped sharply. At best, high-tech agriculture in much of southern Asia has been a temporary measure rather than a long-term solution for feeding a large portion of a world population whose growth is out of control. Furthermore, a number of "miracle" grains have proved to be poor in protein content. Such measures can buy only a little time before the next tidal wave of people comes crashing down on the environment. Experts of the Consultative Group on International Agricultural Research are now refocusing their energy on soil research and biological control of pests and deemphasizing high dependency on chemicals that poison the environment.

But what about the longer-term future, over the next century or more? Feeding so many people may require all available cropland, worked with the greatest efficiency, coupled with the skill of genetic engineers. Can we do it? Right now no one knows the answer.

Most population ecologists feel that the ultimate solution must be population control, not technology designed to accommodate still more growth. According to climatologist Reid A. Bryson, "The alternative to these times of mass starvation and death is to keep population near or below the number that can be supported in the *worst* of times, not in the best of times and not even in 'average' times."

A population expert in India has remarked that most of his upper-class countrymen "would be perfectly happy to see 50 percent of the lower-class Indian population disappear," so rapidly is that nation's population of 860 million growing with a doubling of its size within only 33 years. As early as 1975, India's Minister of Agriculture told a concerned world press that his country's famines and the deaths resulting from them "ought to be thought a blessing rather than a curse."

POLLUTION AND THE ENVIRONMENT

Our race to produce more and more food for more and more people, and to provide increasing amounts of energy, machines, clothing, shelter, and other needs of those ever-increasing numbers of people, means that we are dumping more pollutants into the environment. In recent years scientists have been warning that governments and industry can no longer regard the environment simply as a vast industrial sewer. We have reached the stage when the environment can no longer keep pace in recycling our wastes, as it once did when there were fewer people and less industrial activity.

Our toxic chemical wastes, plastic bags, throw-away bottles, long-lived radioactive wastes from nuclear weapons plants, more radioactive wastes from nuclear power plants, and an endless list of other wastes are accumulating in the environment at an unprecedented and dangerous rate. Forests are being damaged by smog and acid rain. Old toxic waste dumps, some secretly dug by industrial chemical plants, have been discovered under schools and just beneath the surface of housing developments. In some cases, builders were not aware of the dangerous ground beneath their foundations. In others, land developers have bought toxic sites from industry, covered them with a thin layer of ground, and then sold them to unsuspecting buyers.

Crops sometimes are ruined by soil degradation and by water and air pollutants. Many areas, including parts of California and Long Island, New York, face serious drinking water supply problems because of overpopulation. On Long Island, fresh water is being pumped out of the ground faster than it can be replaced naturally by more fresh water. Unusable ocean water is taking its place. In other areas drinking water is contaminated by fertilizer runoff and other pollutants. In Chapter 7 we will have more to say about our responsibility to the environment as opposed to our right to use it thoughtlessly and carelessly. Abusing it is, of course, senseless, because abuse ultimately affects the quality of our lives. So we end up unwittingly abusing ourselves.

Again, spaceship Earth is a closed ecological system. We cannot simply open the hatch and toss our wastes out into space. There is no hatch. Because our wastes must remain on board with us, we must be mindful of how much waste we produce, the kinds of wastes we produce, and how we are to deal with them in the long-term future, not just tomorrow.

Four

THE HUMAN ORGANISM

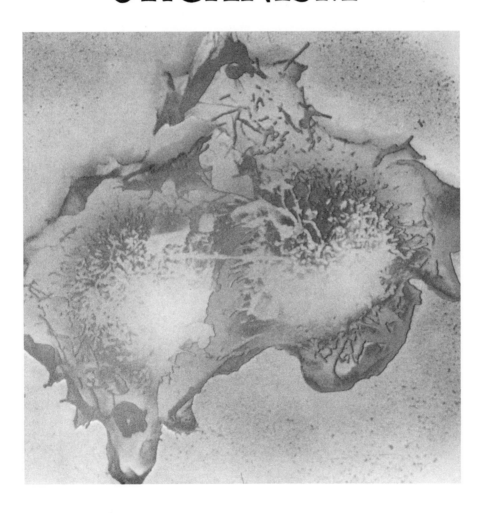

HUMAN EVOLUTION

Modern human beings evolved about a million years ago, and we continue to evolve today. But our ancestry goes back much further than that. Some seventy million years ago, according to the fossil record, small insect-eating mammals branched out into two dozen or more different groups. Among those groups was one called primates. The primates in turn split off into three groups—tree shrews; lemurs and tarsiers; and the new-world monkeys. One of the new-world monkey groups eventually gave rise to the apes and human beings (see diagram).

The members of all three primate groups took to the trees as a way of life. By doing so they avoided competition with other mammals that remained on the ground. To live successfully in the trees required two important adaptations: (1) the evolution of "fingers" and toes with claws (which later became nails in human beings) capable of grasping tree branches; and (2) forward-facing eyes, instead of eyes at the sides of the head. Forward-facing eyes provided much-needed depth perception for life in the trees.

Africa was the scene of the evolution of the primate branch that led to humans. The oldest known ancestor on this branch was an apelike animal weighing about twelve pounds that lived in Egypt some thirty million years ago. It is called *Aegyptopithecus*. A more recent member of our evolutionary ancestors appeared about twenty-five million years ago. Called *Dryopithecus*, it stayed around for fifteen million years before becoming extinct. Its fossil remains have been found in Africa, Europe, and Asia. *Dryopithecus* seems to have spent part of its time in the trees and part on the ground.

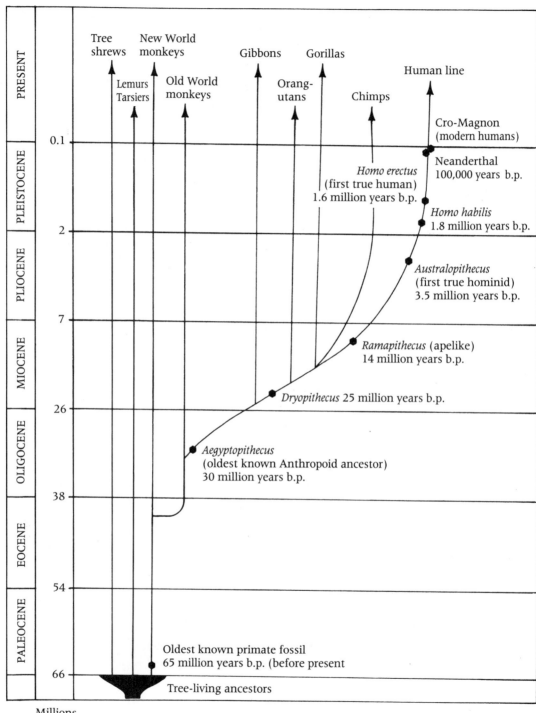

ADAPTIVE RADIATION OF PRIMATES

About fourteen million years ago a being regarded by some as a primitive human, but by others as an advanced ape, evolved and lived in Africa, India, Asia, Greece, Turkey, and Hungary. It was called *Ramapithecus*.

Many fossils of a more recent humanlike group called *Australopithecus* keep turning up in Africa. The first one to be found was the skull of a six-year-old child with distinctly human teeth. It was discovered in South Africa in 1924. The oldest one is 3.5 million years old and was uncovered in Ethiopia in 1974. The bones were of a female who stood about 3 feet 8 inches tall. The anthropologists who found her named her Lucy. In 1986 while digging in Tanzania, Africa, the same researchers found a skull and the limb bones of a descendant of Lucy about 1.8 million years old. The bones were those of a female about thirty years old, who stood about 3 feet tall. Members of her species have been named *Homo habilis*.

Anthropologists think that *Homo habilis* learned to fashion crude tools out of pebbles and that they supplemented their vegetable diet with meat. They lived in regions from Africa to Asia, and in a short 200,000 years (1.6 million years ago) gave rise to the earliest known distinctly human line, called *Homo erectus*, meaning "upright man." Over those 200,000 years, evolution of the human line moved abruptly from a species only 3 feet tall (*Homo habilis*) to one nearly our size (*Homo erectus*).

Although they were well on the way to becoming modern human beings, *Homo erectus* still had telltale apelike features: powerful jaws, a large face, and a prominent brow bone. But apes they were not. They probably wore animal pelts for warmth against the cold and knew how to make fire and to fashion weapons and stone tools. Their brain size also became larger, and their intelligence probably increased enough to give them some power

Opposite: The primates evolved from tree-living ancestors and, according to one interpretation, gave rise to three major groups: tree shrews, prosimians (lemurs and tarsiers), and anthropoids (monkeys, apes, and humans). As new fossil finds are made and analyzed, the primate family tree continues to change with the addition of relatively new members such as *Homo habilis* and *Aegyptopithecus*. Each new primate fossil find is an important event since it may help complete the story of our human ancestry.

of speech. A cave in China used by *Homo erectus* descendants for some 70,000 years revealed that these people were hunters. Among remains found in the cave were cooking hearths, tools, and many bones of the hunters themselves. These people are called Peking Man. Similar fossil finds in Germany are known as Heidelberg Man. All represent about the same stage in human evolution.

The next major event in the story of human evolution is the beginning of the takeover by modern people. The time is some 300,000 years ago, and the last *Homo erectus* types had become extinct. By this time modern human types were living in Africa and Asia, differing little in appearance from populations living there today. But if we met those people on the street we would notice at least some differences. They had jaws somewhat larger than ours, a slightly longer head, and a somewhat larger face. But because they were so much like us, we include them as *Homo sapiens*. The remains of four such types between 300,000 and 200,000 years old have been studied, two from France, one from England, and one from Germany.

The picture of how human beings evolved over the next 200,000 years is still hazy and much debated among anthropologists, although the paleontologist's spade continues to produce new evidence year by year. One group of anthropologists thinks that all modern human beings have as ancestors a population that lived in Africa about 200,000 years ago. Over the next 100,000 years members of that population migrated to other regions, including Europe. As they settled in new regions, they replaced existing populations of other, less able human types. Among those less able groups were Neanderthal people. They had relatively large jaws and lived in the Near East, and still other groups lived in southwest Asia about 60,000 years ago.

By about 35,000 years ago all of the Neanderthals were gone, and no one knows how they met their end. In their place, and populating Europe, Asia, and many other areas of the world, were large groups of small-jawed people just like us, called Cro-Magnon (meaning modern man). Most of the world's human populations have interbred since Cro-Magnon became permanently established, but some may still retain certain characteristics of the Cro-Magnon artists who left their cave paintings for future generations to interpret and admire. Among such groups are the Basque people of northeastern Spain and the Berbers of the Atlas Mountains of North America.

That human beings have evolved from earlier biological groups, which in turn evolved from common ancestors going back some thirty million years, is hard to deny. Our convincing evidence is the fossil record. Less clear are the exact routes that human evolution has followed over the past few scores of millions of years. But each year, as new fossil finds add to the ever-growing body of evidence, our knowledge of our evolutionary past is enriched and our view of that fascinating past is brought into sharper focus.

THE ORIGIN OF HUMAN RACES

Although *Homo sapiens* is the only existing human species today, there are various geographical races of our species. A "race" within any species can be thought of as a group of populations with certain physical and genetic characteristics in common that set the group apart from all other populations of the same species. As Cro-Magnon people increased their numbers and populated virtually every part of the world by about 50,000 years ago, their various populations gradually adapted to various regional environments, and so evolved geographical races.

Populations of all organisms ebb and flow and change in response to changes in the environment, and they have done so throughout the history of life on this planet. Human populations are no exception, because our genes, like those of other species, are subject to environmental pressure. Consequently, human populations living in markedly different environments have adapted differently. For example, the Eskimos' relatively short fingers are thought to be an adaptation to a cold environment. Short fingers have less surface area from which to lose heat than do long fingers, so short fingers tend to reduce the risk of frostbite. People adapted to a hot climate tend to have long limbs, an adaptation that promotes heat loss and so prevents overheating of the body. Inhabitants of the Andes Mountains of South America have evolved relatively large chests and have larger lungs and a larger supply of blood than do people who live at sea level. These features are adaptations to life at high altitude, where oxygen is less available because of the lower atmospheric pressure.

The dark skin of the Negroid race may be an adaptation to protect the skin from the damaging action of ultraviolet radiation, which is more intense near the Equator than in middle and high latitudes. In such an environment, natural selection might have favored those individuals with the ability to produce lots of melanin, the pigment that darkens the skin. In medium and high latitudes where there is relatively less sunlight, a dark skin can be disadvantageous, because an excess of melanin interferes with vitamin D production in the skin, which occurs through the action of sunlight. Therefore, natural selection at those latitudes might have favored individuals with relatively light skin color.

It is hard to pin down the origin and selective advantage (or disadvantage) of certain variations that have been used to characterize the races. Furthermore, such variations are characteristic of *populations*, not *individuals*, and there always will be individuals who cannot be pigeonholed into this or that racial category.

The idea that the modern human geographical races have evolved as a result of population adaptations over thousands of years is hard to challenge, even if some of the causes are not clear. When different populations of the same species go slightly but significantly separate ways in response to different environmental conditions, we call it parallel evolution. But those separate ways have never led to a fixed and unchanging human race.

There is no such things as a "pure" race, meaning one that forever remains the same. Because all human beings belong to the same species, our various populations are capable of interbreeding, and interbreeding has been the rule throughout human history. Time and again, as invaders of one geographical race have conquered a neighboring people, the populations have mixed and their racial distinctions have blurred. According to the evolutionary biologist E. Peter Volpe, "The whole world today is a single large neighborhood. Modern man lives in one great reproductive community."

Races, then, are nothing more than temporary and enlarging collections of genes in a population's gene pool, passing stages in the fleeting evolutionary history of a species.

You sometimes hear people speak of the Italian "race" or the Jewish "race." There is, of course, no such thing. There is a Jewish religion and a Catholic religion, there are people of Italian nationality and of French nationality, but none of these makes up a *race*. You also sometimes hear of the Aryan "race," which is another mistaken idea. Aryans are people who speak languages that are offshoots of the root language Indo-European. Such languages include German, Italian, French, English, and others, and anyone who speaks one of those languages as a native is an Aryan. All such people belong to different cultures, not different races.

NUTRITION AND DIGESTION

NUTRITION. Humans must take in from the environment certain raw materials in order to survive. We need those raw materials as a source of energy and for nutrition, which enables the body to maintain itself and grow. (That is as true for a silk worm and a salamander as it is for you.)

We need three chief classes of food to build the molecules necessary to sustain life: proteins, carbohydrates, and fats. Our body cells process those energy-rich molecules by combining them with the oxygen we breathe. In the process, some biologically useful energy is released to power all our bodily functions, and some is packaged and stored in special chemicals that can be called up and tapped as more energy is needed later. The work done by biologically useful energy includes transporting nutrients into cells and exporting wastes out of cells; moving muscles and other cells; and building new cell parts. A balanced diet of proteins, carbohydrates, and fats is needed for good health.

In addition to proteins, carbohydrates, and fat, living cells need two other kinds of nutrients—minerals and vitamins. Minerals include chemical elements such as calcium, sodium, potassium, phosphorus, iron, and magnesium (and certain others, called trace minerals, that are needed in small amounts).

TABLE OF SELECTED MINERALS

MINERAL	SOURCE	IMPORTANCE
Calcium	Dairy products, shellfish, green leafy vegetables	Strengthens bones and teeth, aids blood clotting and muscle and nerve activity
Phosphorus	Dairy foods, meat, fish, poultry, nuts	(As above) Also present in RNA and DNA; helps store and transfer chemical energy
Iron	Meat, fish, egg yolk, shellfish, beans, legumes, nuts, dried fruits, cereals	Present in blood hemoglobin, carries oxygen to body cells
Iodine	Seafoods, iodized salt, vegetables, cod-liver oil	Needed by thyroid gland to make thyroxin; present in hormones that regulate metabolism
Sodium	Salt (NaCl)	Important to fluid bathing cells; regulates water distribution
Potassium	Present in normal foods we eat	Needed for muscle contraction and nerve impulses
Magnesium	Present in normal foods we eat	Important in bone formation and normal function of muscles and nerves

Vitamins are a class of nutrients that the body cannot make for itself and, therefore, must get from other sources—certain foods, bacteria in our guts, sunlight, or vitamin pills. Unlike fats and proteins, vitamins do not provide energy or serve as building blocks. Instead, they help regulate the pace of our body chemistry.

TABLE OF SELECTED VITAMINS

VITAMIN	SOURCE	IMPORTANCE
Vitamin A	Fish, liver oils	General maintenance
Vitamin D	Liver oils of bony fish, egg yolk, milk, sunlight	Helps build and maintain muscle tone; enables bones to use calcium
Vitamin E	Nuts, seed oils, green vegetables, wheat germ	Needed by RNA, DNA, and red blood cells; helps protect liver
Vitamin K	Spinach, cabbage, liver, intestinal bacteria	Essential for normal blood clotting
Vitamin B_1	Whole-grain cereal, eggs, pork, nuts, liver, yeast	Enables body to break down and use carbohydrates
Vitamin B_2	Yeast, liver, beef, veal, lamb, eggs, peas, beets, asparagus, peanuts	Enables body to break down and use carbohydrates and proteins, especially in cells of the eyes
Niacin	Yeast, meats, liver, fish, whole-grain breads and cereals, peas, beans, nuts	Important in the breakdown of fats; slows production of cholesterol
Vitamin C	Citrus fruits, tomatoes, green vegetables	Aids metabolism in many ways, especially in use of protein; lack causes scurvy, loosening of teeth and swollen gums, bleeding, poor wound healing, and growth retardation
Vitamin B_{12}	Liver, kidney, milk, eggs, cheese, meat	Needed for red blood cell formation; lack affects nervous system

DIGESTION.   The digestive process is similar in virtually all animals. Food is taken in, ground up, and mixed with various digestive juices called enzymes. The resulting nutrient solutions are then absorbed and carried by the blood to all of the organism's living cells.

Within seconds after you take a bite of an apple, while you are still chewing, digestion begins. As your chewing breaks down the food mechanically, salivary glands pour digestive juice enzymes into your mouth, lubricating and breaking down the food chemically. For example, the salivary enzyme ptyalin breaks down carbohydrate molecules and converts them to the sugar maltose. But food stays in your mouth too short a time to be completely broken down chemically.

Swallowing moves food down through the esophagus into the stomach. Muscular action of the stomach further breaks down the food mechanically. At the same time, more substances/agents attack it chemically—hydrochloric acid and the enzyme pepsin, for example. The hydrochloric acid increases acidity so that pepsin can function in breaking apart protein molecules. After the stomach has converted its contents to a juice, the juice is forced into the small intestine.

Food entering the small intestine is attacked by three more digestive juices containing more enzymes that split fat, sugar, and proteins. Juices from the liver, gall bladder, and pancreas also attack the food solution and help break it into nutrient molecules.

The nutrient molecules are then absorbed and enter the blood stream. Day and night the blood carries a continuous supply of nutrients around the body to feed all of its living cells.

Drained of nutrients, the leftover food passes into the large intestine and eventually is expelled as waste matter. About one day elapses between the time your dinner enters your body and the time some of it leaves as waste. The food spends about six hours of that time in your stomach.

Digestion accomplishes the same thing in all animals: It breaks down large (food) molecules into smaller (nutrient) molecules that can be transported throughout the body and used as an energy source to drive the endless number of chemical reactions that build new body parts and repair worn or damaged ones.

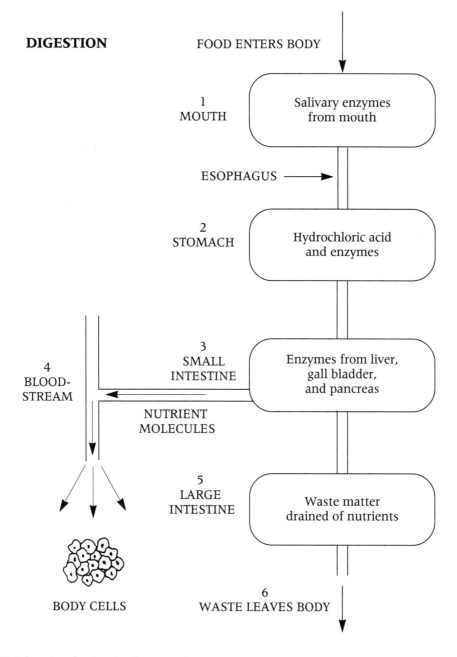

DIGESTION

FOOD ENTERS BODY

1
MOUTH — Salivary enzymes from mouth

ESOPHAGUS →

2
STOMACH — Hydrochloric acid and enzymes

3
SMALL INTESTINE — Enzymes from liver, gall bladder, and pancreas

4
BLOOD-STREAM

NUTRIENT MOLECULES

5
LARGE INTESTINE — Waste matter drained of nutrients

BODY CELLS

6
WASTE LEAVES BODY

(1) Digestion begins in the mouth when enzymes are mixed with chewed food. (2) More enzymes and hydrochloric acid are mixed with food as it is further broken down by the stomach's muscle action. (3 and 4) Nutrient molecules leave small intestine and enter bloodstream. Waste matter then passes through large intestine (5) and exits the body (6) some 24 hours after eating.

RESPIRATION

Oxygen ignites and "fires" the fuel of our bodies. The fuel we need to stay alive is the sugar glucose, which is carried by the blood to our body cells. Glucose is supplied to us by the breakdown of larger food molecules during digestion. That process of chemical breakdown depends on a continuous supply of oxygen throughout our lives. The "burning" is a slow combining of oxygen and glucose that takes place in our body cells. When a lump of coal or a piece of wood burns, oxygen combines rapidly with the substance that is burning. A wood fire is rapid oxidation, whereas a biological "fire" is slow oxidation.

All organisms that require oxygen for life have evolved various ways of getting oxygen. Fish, shrimp, and lobsters, for example, have gills that remove oxygen from the water. Other animals rely on lungs to remove oxygen from the air. Respiration, however, involves more than just the intake of oxygen to burn glucose. When the glucose is burned, the gas carbon dioxide (CO_2) is produced and must be given off as waste. Water also is produced.

$$C_6H_{12}O_6 \quad + \quad 6O_2 \quad \rightarrow \quad 6CO_2 \quad + \quad 6H_2O$$

| Glucose | Oxygen | Carbon dioxide | Water |

Our lungs live in a protective cage formed by our ribs. We breathe without having to think about it through the automatic action of certain chest muscles and the diaphragm. As the diaphragm pushes upward beneath our lungs, it forces air out of the lungs, causing us to exhale. When the diaphragm contracts and withdraws from the lungs, it causes the lungs to pull air in and we inhale.

Inside the lungs are millions of tiny air bladders called alveoli. Each one is in contact with tiny blood vessels. The air we inhale contains about 20 percent oxygen; the rest is mostly nitrogen. Oxygen molecules taken in during each breath are captured by the alveoli and passed into the blood stream. They immediately become attached to red blood cells, which carry the oxygen throughout the body and release it to our cells. At the same time respiring cells take in oxygen, they give off carbon dioxide to the blood. The carbon dioxide is carried back to the lungs, passed off to the alveoli, into the lung cavity, and then exhaled to the outside. Because living cells respire day and night, carrying out their many chemical activities, they must be supplied with oxygen day and night or the organism will die.

In broad outline, three body systems work together to keep us alive: The digestive system provides the nutrient glucose "fuel"; the respiratory system provides the oxygen "spark"; and the blood of the circulatory system carries both to the cell "furnaces" and at the same time removes the carbon dioxide "ash."

CIRCULATION

Your fist is about the size and shape of the human heart. Weighing less than a pound, the heart is a four-chambered muscle that pumps our ten pints of blood around and around the blood circulatory system of arteries and veins and capillaries. The pumping begins when we are a fetus about sixteen weeks old and continues without stopping until the moment we die. The blood that surges and pulses through the 60,000 miles of living pipeline of soft tubing carries a host of nutrient provisions to our cells and removes metabolic garbage from them.

In one hour the heart's rhythmic contractions pump about 540 pounds of blood. In one day the heart beats 103,680 times and pumps more than 5,000 quarts nonstop. In an average human lifetime the heart beats about three *billion* times without rest.

The blood flows along a one-way pipeline. After leaving the heart it is pumped into and through a system of branching arteries that end as thousands of very small tube networks called capillaries. Arterial blood is rich in oxygen, which it has picked up from the lungs. The oxygen is fed to the body's cells through the thin and porous capillary walls. At the same time, cells unload their waste gas, carbon dioxide, into the blood. The blood then

CIRCULATION

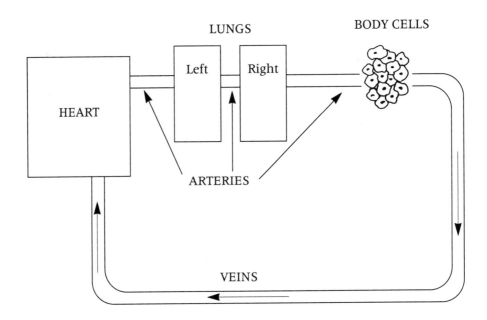

Our blood flows along a one-way pipeline of soft tubing some 60,000 miles long. It is pumped out of the heart through arteries to the lungs where it picks up oxygen. Blood then leaves the lungs and carries the oxygen to all of the body's living cells. At the same time, the blood carries away the waste gas carbon dioxide from our cells through our veins. Pumped once again to the lungs, the blood unloads its waste carbon dioxide and picks up more oxygen.

leaves the capillaries and enters a network of veins for a return trip to the lungs. As it unloads its cargo of carbon dioxide into the lungs for exhalation, the blood collects a new supply of oxygen. The oxygen attaches to the hemoglobin in our red blood cells and so is made ready for delivery to the body cells once again as the enriched blood returns to the heart and is again pumped back into the system of arteries. Because a system of valves prevents the blood from sloshing back and forth during its journey, it flows in one direction.

The products of digestion, molecules of sugar, amino acids, and other nutrients, are carried by the blood and delivered to our body cells through the tiny capillary pores. But the blood has other cargo as well. When you examine a drop of blood you can see it separate into two parts—solid particles and a clear liquid. The fluid part of the blood is called plasma and serves as a "river" to carry the solid-particle "barges." There are three types of solid particles: (1) red blood cells, which carry oxygen and carbon dioxide; (2) white blood cells, which combat germs and other foreign bodies; and (3) platelets, which help stop bleeding by forming blood clots.

In addition to collecting carbon dioxide waste from the body cells, our blood collects other waste matter, solids that cannot be expelled by the lungs. How does the body's waste management system handle all this unwanted cargo?

As the blood flows through the kidneys it passes through many clusters of capillaries. As it does, waste products pass from the blood into the capillaries, which then pass the wastes into some half million structures called nephrons. The nephrons have a total of about fifty miles of tiny waste-collecting tubes. The tubes send the wastes to the bladder where they collect as urine, which is then periodically drained from the body. While ridding itself of waste matter, the blood also gives up various nutrient molecules needed by the body. The kidneys are able to separate these useful molecules from the waste and channel them back into the blood for reuse.

THE NERVOUS SYSTEM

Day and night the human body acts as an electronic circuit board that puts the most complex computer to shame. We cry "Eureka!" when the solution to a problem suddenly and unexpectedly occurs. Airline pilots' ears are bombarded with rapid-fire instructions from air traffic controllers, and they must react to these terse messages immediately while they monitor dozens of dials and lights. When you touch a hot object, you instantly jerk your hand away before you can even think about the action. Our every thought, emotion, word uttered or heard, and step taken are controlled by our nervous system, which protects and guides us, ceaselessly processes information—even as we sleep—and otherwise keeps our minds and bodies functioning.

The brain and the spinal cord are the control centers of the nervous system. Twelve pairs of cranial nerves from the brain are linked with our eyes, ears, throat, and certain organs in the chest and stomach regions. Thirty-one pairs of spinal cord nerves extend through openings up and down the vertebral column. They branch and rebranch and, with the cranial nerves, form a network that reaches every bone, every organ, every tissue system, and every square millimeter of skin from head to toe.

Nerve impulses are electrochemical signals that travel back and forth throughout the nerve network through the basic units of the nervous system—neurons, or nerve cells. The human body has about 10 billion neurons; depending on their location and function, neurons range from a fraction of an inch long to five or six feet long.

There are three major classes of neurons—sensory neurons, motor neurons, and interneurons. The sensory neurons inform the brain about what's happening to the body, inside and out. Sensory pick-up stations, called receptors, are at or near the skin surface, on the tongue, in the eyes and ears, in our muscles, and at other locations inside the body. When you walk barefooted over hot beach sand, temperature receptors in your feet send nerve impulses along the train of sensory nerves to the spinal column and from there to the brain. The brain considers the matter of the hot sand and sends nerve impulses back down the spinal column and then along motor neurons to your leg and foot muscles that make you start hopping about in an attempt to keep your feet off the hot sand. Sensory neurons, together with their associated receptors, sense all sorts of conditions that affect the body's well-being and transmit the information to the brain. Motor neurons then carry nerve impulses, initiated by the brain, to muscles and glands that follow the brain's instructions—to correct a potentially bad situation, for example. Connecting neurons, which make up 99 percent of all our neurons, shuttle nerve signals back and forth between the brain, spinal cord, and other parts of the body.

Sometimes the body must respond instantly to avoid damage—when you decide to stick your finger in a flame to find out how hot it is, for example. Receptors in your finger cause its sensory nerves to fire "Danger!" signals up toward the brain. But the signal is so strong that the spinal cord takes over and, without consulting the brain, sends nerve impulses along motor nerves to activate muscles that cause you to jerk your finger out of the flame automatically. Such reactions are called reflex actions. When your knee is tapped just below the knee cap, your lower leg jerks forward. This reflex action comes in handy when you are walking along a woods trail and trip on a small tree root. The jolt acts like a tap on the knee and your leg automatically and instantly shoots forward and prevents you from falling.

REPRODUCTION

In humans, as in most species of plants and animals, new individuals are produced only by the union of reproductive cells called sex cells, or germ cells, or gametes. The union of an egg cell and a sperm cell is called fertilization. A newly fertilized egg contains two sets of genetic information— one set from the mother and one from the father. In both males and females the organs of sexual reproduction within the body are linked by tubes for communication with the outside world.

IN FEMALES the primary organs of reproduction are the ovaries, which produce egg cells. From about the age of 13 to about age 45, females produce egg cells, one egg being released about every 28 or so days. At the time of egg release, called ovulation, the egg leaves the ovary and works its way down a tubelike oviduct that leads into the birth chamber, the uterus. The uterus leads to the outside of the female's body through an opening called the vagina, or birth canal.

HUMAN REPRODUCTIVE SYSTEM

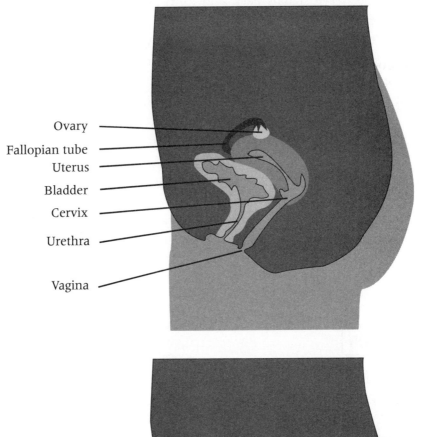

- Ovary
- Fallopian tube
- Uterus
- Bladder
- Cervix
- Urethra
- Vagina

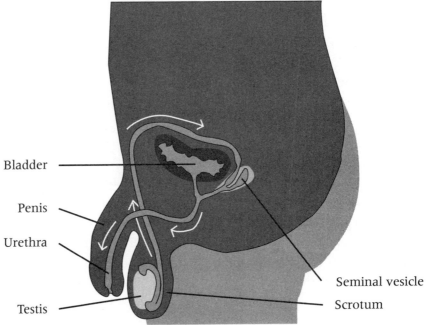

- Bladder
- Penis
- Urethra
- Testis
- Seminal vesicle
- Scrotum

IN MALES the primary organs of reproduction are the testes, which begin to produce sperm cells from about age 13 or 15. The testes are held in the scrotum, a sac that hangs outside the body. Thousands of tiny tubes within the testes produce the sperm cells. The tubes lead into the urethra, which continues in the penis leading to the outside. The testes' location outside the body is very important because sperm cells require a temperature slightly lower than body temperature to remain healthy. On their way into the penis the sperm cells are bathed and mixed with glandular fluids that provide the sperm cells with nourishment, give them chemical protection, and provide a fluid medium (semen) through which the sperm cells can swim by beating their whiplike tails back and forth.

CONCEPTION. When a male and female become sexually aroused and mate, the male inserts his erect penis into the female's vagina. Sexual excitement causes blood to surge into the penis, making it firm and erect. Successive pelvic thrusts further excite the male and, at the peak of excitement, cause millions of sperm cells to be ejaculated out through the penis into the vagina. Each sperm cell propels itself from the vagina into the uterus and then along the oviducts. Muscular contractions of the uterus help move the sperm cells along. On meeting an egg cell, one and only one of the millions of sperm cells penetrates the egg in the act of fertilization. After about forty-eight hours sperm cells lose their ability to fertilize an egg cell.

The fertilized egg continues down the oviduct into the uterus, where it attaches to the uterus wall. If left undisturbed, the fertilized egg, now called a zygote, receives nourishment from the mother and undergoes development into a new individual. The female is now said to be pregnant.

CONTRACEPTION. Methods designed to prevent pregnancy (contraception) are thousands of years old. "Magic brews" have been swallowed by women to prevent pregnancy—sheep urine and camel saliva, for example. They didn't work. A small sponge soaked with lemon juice and inserted into the vagina sometimes worked, when the citric acid killed the sperm cells. Withdrawing the penis from the vagina just before ejaculation also worked, but only sometimes.

The surest way to avoid pregnancy is to avoid sexual intercourse for life, as dictated by certain religious orders. Another way, but a much less certain one, is to avoid intercourse from about the eleventh to the seventeenth day after the onset of bleeding during the menstrual cycle. Called the rhythm method, it is unreliable because the menstrual cycle varies so much. Many women and men have minor surgery to prevent eggs and sperm from ever getting together. Women can have the tubes from their oviducts severed and tied off, which prevents sperm cells from reaching the egg cells in the upper oviducts. Men can block passage of their sperm cells to the penis by having the tubes leading to the urethra cut and sealed. Such surgery in both males and females usually can be reversed successfully so that both are again fertile.

The use of a condom, a rubber sac fitted over the penis just before sexual intercourse, is another method of preventing sperm from entering the female. A female version of a condom is the diaphragm, a rubber disc inserted into the vagina that blocks entrance to the uterus. A diaphragm is used in conjunction with a jelly substance (phenyl mercuric acetate, for instance) designed to form a seal around the diaphragm and to kill sperm cells.

Still another contraceptive device is the once popular IUD, or intrauterine device. IUDs, small pieces of metal shaped as coils, hoops, or bows, are inserted into the uterus, where they remain for as long as the wearer chooses. They prevent a fertilized egg from successfully attaching to the wall of the uterus and undergoing development.

A number of birth control methods depend on sex hormone pills that either interfere with egg production or prevent the fertilized egg from attaching to the uterine wall. Another method involves the insertion of tiny capsules of sex hormone beneath a female's skin; the hormone feeds very slowly into the blood stream and interferes with egg production. One implant lasts for about five years. The capsules can be removed by minor surgery at any time to restore fertility. Birth control agents designed to suppress sperm production have been far less successful than similar methods designed for the female reproductive system.

DEVELOPMENT

When an egg cell and a sperm cell fuse in fertilization within the body of a female, a new individual called a zygote is formed and the beginning of a new human life is set in motion.

The zygote migrates into the uterus and three days later becomes implanted within the uterine wall, where it receives nourishment from the mother's blood. It also receives whatever harmful agents may be present in the mother's body—alcohol and other drugs, for example. It is extremely important for the mother to keep herself in the healthiest possible condition all the time she is carrying her baby. Alcohol- and drug-addicted mothers can pass their addictions on to their babies. Children born of alcoholic mothers may be mentally retarded, disfigured, and remain handicapped throughout life.

For the next 266 days, or nine months, this new individual will continue to depend on its mother for nourishment, warmth, and protection.

Within seventy-two hours after fertilization, the zygote's single cell divides, and those two cells in turn divide until there are sixteen cells all very much alike. After about two weeks, when implantation is complete, the zygote is called an embryo. By the end of the first month the embryo consists of millions of cells but is only one-eighth of an inch long. During this time a thin-tissue sac, called a placenta, encloses the embryo but permits nutrients and oxygen from the mother to pass through to the embryo and permits carbon dioxide and other wastes from the embryo to pass out into the mother's blood stream to be discarded. Before the end of the first month, an embryo's brain has begun to form, as have a rudimentary mouth, sightless eyes, primitive kidneys, blood cells, and limb buds that will become arms and legs. The embryo is still smaller than a pea.

During the second month bone tissue begins to form, tiny fingers and toes appear, the head and brain develop rapidly, the circulatory system develops, and reproductive organs form enough so that the sex of the embryo can be determined. By the end of the second month the embryo

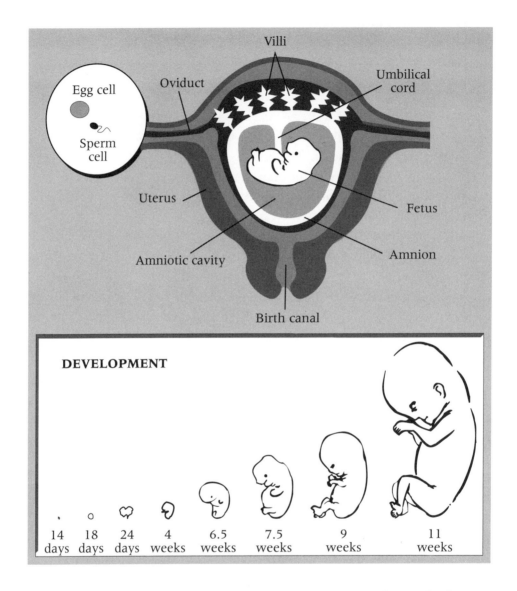

An egg cell from the female and a sperm cell from the male fuse in fertilization and produce a new individual, a zygote, which rapidly develops into an embryo. Attached to the uterus wall, the embryo exchanges materials (nutrients and wastes) with the mother through the placenta. Over the 9-month period of development, the embryo-fetus continues development in the pool of fluid within the amnion sac. The sketches of embryonic development from 14 days to 11 weeks are shown actual size.

is more or less human in appearance, about two inches long, and is renamed a fetus.

The third month sees movement of the fetus within its placental sac. It "breathes" surrounding fluid into its lungs, displays swallowing motions, smiles, frowns, and makes faces. Its bones begin to grow together toward their joints. Although all its organ systems have been formed, the fetus is still too young to survive if removed from the mother.

During the fourth and fifth months the fetus holds up its head, makes strong muscular movements, and responds to general body movements of the mother, sometimes by kicking vigorously. Because the skeleton of the fetus develops rapidly during this period, the mother must supply large amounts of calcium and other bone-building materials.

At six months the fetus is very active, kicking and turning this way and that except when it sleeps. It has become large and demanding of nutrients, has all appearances of a baby, and may survive if removed from the mother's body and supplied with life-support systems. In the last three months development and growth continue. About 260 days after fertilization the placenta begins to break down, which changes the environment of the fetus. When that happens, growth slows and the fetus drops head first toward the bottom of the uterus. By the end of the ninth month, all its organs have made the final changes that enable the infant to survive when its mother gives birth.

PUBERTY AND ADOLESCENCE

PUBERTY. When young people enter their teens their bodies undergo major chemical and physical changes that begin to prepare them for adulthood. The change is triggered by action of a part of the nervous system called the hypothalamus. This small cluster of nerve cells regulates heart beat, breathing, body temperature, and the sleep cycle. It also turns on the flow of hormones that prepare a typical 12-year-old for sexual activity—called puberty.

In girls the onset of puberty is marked by the beginning of menstruation, the development of the breasts and pubic hair, a change in skeletal structure (especially a widening of the hips), and the development of fat deposits that produce a rounded, feminine shape. These changes are brought on mainly by a group of female hormones called estrogens, which are produced in the ovaries. Several months later a second female hormone, progesterone (also produced by the ovaries), becomes active. It changes the uterus by making it capable of supporting and nourishing an embryo. Puberty and adolescence prepare females for childbearing—wider hips for the ease of carrying and delivering a child, fat deposits to serve as a food supply for the embryo in times of food shortages, and breasts for feeding the newborn infant.

In boys the onset of puberty is marked by rapid muscular and skeletal growth and the appearance of pubic hair; in addition, boys become energetic and exhibit aggressive behavior. Boys also develop a deeper voice and facial hair. Hormones that help trigger these changes are called androgens and are produced in the testes. The most active androgen is testosterone. In both sexes an insufficient amount of sex hormones results in stunted growth and infertility.

ADOLESCENCE.   After puberty has begun, adolescence continues for a few more years until the young person has attained full strength and stature. The sexual changes that ready the body for reproduction develop at the same time as the secondary sex characteristics (skeletal change, speeded growth, and so on). Facial hair and a deep voice are a boy's signal to others that he has become a man. The badge of maturity for girls is their newly enlarged breasts, a "feminine figure," and menstruation.

During this important time of transition from child to adult, the adolescent is faced with many psychological adjustments. "Who am I now that I'm changing?" "Am I still the same as my friends, or am I growing different?" "Am I better or worse than others?" "Should I keep on respecting my parents as I did as a kid?'' ''What kind of people are my parents anyway?''

Many other new and probing questions reflecting a new kind of curiosity and insecurity bombard the adolescent and demand new decisions and judgments, not only about family and friends, but about the world at large, about **Life**. However, the adolescent is not yet prepared through the experience of living to answer such profound questions wisely. More immediate concerns are ''good looks,'' ''popularity,'' ''physical build.'' ''Are my breasts too small?'' ''Do I have a good figure?'' ''Will the girls like my new haircut?''

Those who reach physical maturity relatively late are usually the most anxious about being accepted by others. According to psychological tests, boys are more dissatisfied than girls with late physical development, and boys who mature late tend to feel rejected, rebellious, and aggressive, and may be more dependent for psychological support from their family and friends.

Another source of conflict within adolescents stems from the different pace at which girls and boys reach maturity. Girls enter puberty sooner than boys do and begin the psychological changes sooner. According to surveys of junior high schools, girls are about two years ahead of boys in physical development. Many girls have already reached puberty when they enter junior high school, but many boys don't reach puberty until they enter senior high school.

The result of these differences is that many boys and girls who have grown up together miss the opportunity to know each other at the same level of development at the same time. How many boys sorrowfully see the love of their life whisked away by a male a few or several years older, simply because the girl was ''ready'' and the boy was not?

Adolescents experience a no-man's land, teetering between psychological and economic dependency on family and the biological need and readiness to be independent. Controlled and supported by parents, adolescents nevertheless are held responsible for their actions. Although they are biologically ready to become parents, economically and psychologically they usually are not ready.

THE OVARIAN AND MENSTRUAL CYCLES

Each woman is born with about 400,000 reproductive structures called follicles within her two ovaries. The ovaries' follicles are the sites of egg production. During the thirty to forty years a healthy female is capable of reproduction, once every twenty-eight or so days, on the average, an egg-producing (ovarian) cycle begins, and with it an accompanying (menstrual) cycle of activity in the uterus. Only about 400 of the original 400,000 follicles produce eggs during a woman's reproductive years. The rest simply degenerate. When a woman reaches her forties, the eggs released are some 40 years old and not as healthy as they were when the woman was in her teens and twenties. Consequently, women who give birth relatively late in life have a greater risk of producing infants with a variety of disorders, including malformation and mental retardation.

The monthly ovarian cycle begins when hormones called FSH and LH are released from the pituitary gland, and estrogen hormones are released by the ovaries. This barrage of hormones causes a follicle and its egg to mature, during which time the relatively high blood level of estrogens also causes the lining of the uterus to thicken and soften. Next, estrogen production slows while LH production quickens. This causes the follicle to rupture and release its egg (ovum), which then becomes available for fertilization. Relieved of its egg, the follicle is changed into a structure called a corpus luteum, which begins to produce estrogens and the hormone progesterone. The production of these hormones helps stimulate the thickening of the uterus wall and stops release of FSH and LH by the pituitary.

The egg liberated by an ovary is moved along a fallopian tube (oviduct) toward the uterus, taking about four days to make the journey. Meanwhile the corpus luteum degenerates if the egg is not fertilized by a sperm cell. With the corpus luteum now inactive, blood levels of estrogens and progesterone fall, which leads to a deterioration of the newly formed soft tissue lining the uterine wall. Blood and decayed tissue begin to drain out of the uterus and through the vagina. Menstruation has begun and continues for three to five days, although there is much individual variation from one woman to the next. Cramps sometimes felt during menstruation are caused by contractions of the muscular walls of the uterus.

If the egg is fertilized on its way toward the uterus, the corpus luteum does not degenerate. Instead it remains active by interrupting both the ovarian and menstrual cycles and preventing destruction of the nutrient-rich lining of the uterus. Therefore, the uterus is prepared once every twenty-eight days to receive, nourish, and otherwise promote the development of a zygote into an embryo and then into a fetus.

With the decay of the uterine wall, blood levels of FSH once again rise and stimulate development of a new follicle and its egg, starting a new ovarian cycle.

THE IMMUNE SYSTEM

Although our bodies have many natural defenses against diseases caused by viruses, fungi, bacteria, animal parasites, and other agents, we usually "catch" at least one cold a year and maybe a viral infection or two that keep us on the run for a day or so. How does the body combat and overcome disease and so maintain itself in a more or less steady state of well-being?

We have a number of natural barriers that ward off disease agents, including the skin, tears and saliva that wash away foreign particles, and stomach juices (and, in women, vaginal secretions) whose acid content kills disease invaders. But more remarkable than all those defense barriers is the body's immune system.

Our immune system performs three major tasks: (1) It recognizes disease agents that invade the body and then locates and destroys them; (2) it develops an ability to single out a specific disease agent, to distinguish it from other similar agents, and to design a killing strategy for the specific agent; and (3) for future needs, it remembers, recognizes, and again defeats a previous disease agent adversary, the mechanism we call immunity.

The body's white blood cells—especially those called lymphocytes—perform those three jobs when all is well with our bodies. The lymphocytes circulate throughout the body and are brought to trouble areas by the blood stream and by another system of vessels called the lymph system. All along the lymph circulation are storage bundles called nodes that contain large numbers of lymphocytes. The technical name for disease agents is antigens. When a certain kind of antigen invades the body, the lymphocytes immediately identify it and undergo cell division to produce large numbers of destructive "weapons" called antibodies, which are a special kind of protein made by the blood.

Sometimes antibodies attach to antigens, like pieces of a jigsaw puzzle, and so neutralize the disease agent. Other times antibodies puncture the cell wall of a bacterium and so destroy the bacterium. Still other antibodies round up concentrations of antigens, which the circulatory system can then easily flush out.

There are two types of antibodies—B-cells and T-cells. The B-cells protect us, or provide immunity, against antigens in the circulatory system and are made in our bones. The T-cells identify and reject transplanted skin or organs such as a transplanted kidney or liver provided by a donor. T-cells also provide us with immunity to cancer cells and attack certain bacteria, viruses, and fungi.

Four types of T-cells are known. One group, called helper T-cells, enables the other T-cells, and most B-cells, to work; they are essential to a healthy immune system. It is those helper T-cells that the AIDS virus (HIV) destroys. AIDS stands for "Acquired Immune Deficiency Syndrome." When a person becomes infected with the AIDS virus, the immune system breaks down and the person becomes an easy and defenseless target for many disease agents, including certain unusual forms of cancer. The AIDS virus also may attack certain cells in the brain and cause neurological problems.

By the late 1980s more than 1.5 million Americans had been infected by the AIDS virus. AIDS is most widespread in central Africa and has been reported in more than 100 other countries worldwide. Many of those infected with AIDS show no signs of the disease, do not know they are infected, and can infect others. To date there is no known cure or preventive vaccine for AIDS, making AIDS one of the most serious epidemics the world has known.

A person suffering from AIDS exhibits fever, diarrhea, a general wasting away, and swollen lymph nodes. First described in 1981, HIV in the United States first attacked homosexual and bisexual men. But the virus can be transmitted to anyone who has sexual contact with a person of either sex who has been infected by the virus. Intravenous drug users who share injection needles and people who receive blood transfusions also may risk getting the virus. Researchers have identified the AIDS virus in several body fluids—blood, semen, saliva, tears, urine, brain fluid, breast milk, and certain vaginal secretions. But strong evidence indicates that the AIDS virus is passed from one person to another by only three major routes: (1) through sexual intercourse; (2) through blood sharing; and (3) from an infected mother to her child before or during birth.

There is no scientific evidence that AIDS is spread through ordinary nonsexual conduct. Health workers who care for AIDS patients, including physicians and nurses, know of no instances of a worker getting AIDS through normal and routine contacts with AIDS patients. Likewise, there are no known cases of a family member getting AIDS from an infected husband, child, or mother through normal and routine contacts. Also, laboratory studies discredit fears that the AIDS virus can be transmitted by insect bites, such as a mosquito bite.

A person who has just been infected with the AIDS virus may not show any symptoms. But symptoms may appear gradually from six months to as much as eight years later. Twenty-six percent to 46 percent of people infected with AIDS develop full-blown signs of the disease within about seven years. Death almost always follows within one to two years. The danger of the seven-year nonsymptomatic or mildly symptomatic period, of course, is that the infected person has about seven years to unknowingly, or knowingly, pass the virus on to others.

VACCINATION. What happens when we get a vaccination? We are inoculated with a vaccine in order to improve the immune system's ability to protect us against this or that specific disease antigen.

Some vaccines contain living antigens of a disease, but the dose is too small to cause the disease. Others contain dead antigens, which accomplish the same thing. The shot "teaches" the immune system to be on the lookout for such antigens in the future, so that a second or third exposure will result in a rapid and forceful response by the lymphocytes of the immune system. Booster shots may be required from time to time, depending on the vaccine.

A person with a weak immune system may have problems with certain vaccines—mild fevers, muscle aches, and tenderness at the site of inoculation. But control of serious disease by vaccination is well worth such risks of temporary discomfort. Among the exceptionally effective vaccines are those for poliomyelitis, measles, mumps, rubella, and influenza. Because influenza organisms tend to change year by year, many people get flu vaccinations every year. Although virtually all vaccines are specific for a certain disease, genetic engineers are developing multipurpose vaccines that protect against two or more quite different ailments.

AGING AND DEATH

Every species seems to have its maximum life span, at the end of which is death for its individuals. But life spans among individuals of the same species vary considerably, for a variety of reasons.

Aging begins sooner than most of us realize, if we consider the beginning of an organ's loss of performance as its onset of aging. Vision, for example, begins to decline when we are in our teens, as does hearing. Muscular strength peaks between twenty and thirty and then declines gradually. Our lungs' ability to transfer oxygen to the blood decreases from 4 liters a minute at age twenty to 1.5 liters a minute at age seventy-five.

Other signs of aging include a gradual decline in kidney function, a buildup of fat tissue in blood vessels (which slows blood flow), and a gradual decline in the immune system's ability to fight disease. Disorders in the

MAXIMUM LIFE SPANS FOR VARIOUS SPECIES

SPECIES	LIFE SPAN IN YEARS
Sequoia	several thousand
Tortoise	150
Human	115
Elephant	78
Horse	40
Lion	35
Cow	30
Parakeet	30
Cat	28
Dog	26
Giant spider	24
Sheep	15
Rabbit	12
Sea horse	6
White bat	2
Annual plant	1

immune system seem to produce antibodies that destroy the body's own tissues. Muscles and joints become less flexible, the muscles and bones slowly lose mass, and our energy levels slow. In women, sometime between ages forty-five and fifty-five, changes in the production of sex hormones cause both the ovarian and menstrual cycles to stop. When people reach their sixties, some notice that they can no longer remember things as well as before. Some people who retire because of ill health or because their companies force them to, undergo deep depression, which may speed the aging process.

Although some humans live beyond age one hundred, most do not. The average life expectancy for people in the United States and certain other industrial societies is about seventy-five. But in other cultures life expectancy is as low as thirty-five. Over the years life expectancy in the rich nations has increased for a number of reasons, improvement in diet and avoidance of drug abuse (including alcohol) also are important ways to prevent shaving years off our lives.

We do not have a good understanding of the biology of aging, or of its causes. For example, is the slow decline in the immune system a result of aging or a cause of aging? Is the gradual accumulation of toxic waste products of metabolism a cause or a result of aging? Biologists generally agree that certain outside influences, such as ionizing radiation, probably combine with the internal biological events just described to trigger the aging process and carry it to the ultimate stage of death. They also generally agree that our genes probably, in some way yet to be discovered, program the aging process through instructions to the brain. If we can decode those instructions it might be possible to override them and so extend our life span well beyond the age of one hundred so that as individuals we can lead significantly longer, productive lives.

Five

HUMAN
BEHAVIOR

NATURE OR NURTURE?

What makes each of us the kind of person we are? Do the genes that we inherit from our parents determine how we are to behave throughout life? Or do the millions of learning experiences we encounter in the home, in school, in church, from our friends, and from everything we watch on television and read determine how we behave?

Many years ago some students of human behavior proposed that our genes (nature) most influenced our behavior. As examples of such influence, they cited our reproductive and sexual drives that make us act in certain ways instinctively. Another group disagreed, saying that our environment (nurture) most influenced and molded us as individuals. Today we look to both our genetic makeup and our social and physical environment to account for the ways we behave. A behavioral scientist might put it this way: *The ways our behavior develops are determined by our social experiences within the context of our inherited genetic potential.*

The moment we are born we become part of a social and cultural setting. We continuously experience instructions and models of behavior through our family, classmates, friends, teachers, and sports or media heroes. All of this instruction is channeled through whatever language we are taught. In short, we are taught to think and behave through example, through rewards and punishment. We eagerly learn and mimic speech patterns, adopt favorite words and "in" expressions and styles of dress, learn to perform body language, and learn to laugh at certain things and frown on certain others. These behaviors become a deep part of us; we are not even aware that we are "behaving." And anyone who behaves differently from the way those in our group behave is immediately thought of as an "outsider" and looked on with suspicion.

All cultures have identifying webs of behavioral patterns, and each culture differs from all others. Even within a single culture, subcultures have different, often conflicting behavior patterns. City "gangs" are subcultures of a larger community culture. And community cultures in turn are subcultures of the larger city culture, and so on up to the levels of state, geographical region, and nation.

In addition to culturally oriented behavior, we seem to share certain behaviors with cultures far removed from our own. For example, virtually all cultures condemn rape, sexual intercourse among family members, violence or theft among one's family, and cannibalism. (There are, of course, exceptions to the widespread condemnation of such behaviors.)

HOW WE INTERPRET THE WORLD: THE SENSES

A large measure of our knowledge of the world comes from the way we sense it through the windows of our five external senses—seeing, hearing, touching, smelling, and tasting. The other major way we acquire knowledge about the world is through learning. The brain transforms the four classes of external sense stimuli (light for seeing, sound for hearing, pressure for touching, and chemical perception for smelling and tasting) into meaningful impressions of the world.

We have internal senses as well: hunger, thirst, fatigue, pain, and our "sense" of balance. Although our internal senses tell us little about the outside world, they are important to the body's well-being.

Evolution through natural selection has designed the sensory apparatus of each species for survival in its particular ecological niche. Although knowledge about a certain aspect of the environment may be essential to one species, it may be useless to another. A dog's major window on the world is its keen sense of smell. We cannot even imagine the symphony of

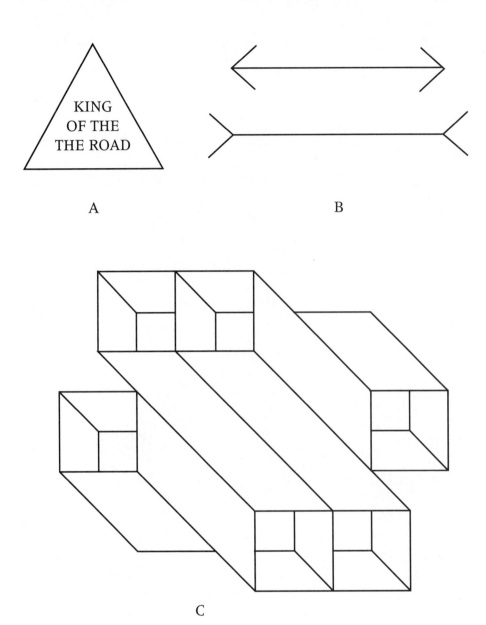

A

B

C

The world is not always the way it seems to be. Sometimes the brain misinterprets signals sent to it by the eye. Read the words in the triangle (A). Read them again, this time out loud. Did you read them incorrectly the first time? Why? Which of the two lines in (B) is longer? Measure them. Stare at figure (C). What does it do?

How can this stream high on one of the rock faces on Mt. Washington, N.H. flow down along the ridge of rock without spilling over the edges? (For the answer, turn the photograph upside down.)

odors sampled by a dog during a walk through the woods. And the dog, with only a minimal ability to see the world in color, cannot imagine the symphony of red, violet, orange, green, and yellow colors perceived by our eyes.

Each of our sense organs is made up of sense cells ranging in number from one to millions. The cells transform the mechanical energy of pressure involved in touch, or the chemical energy involved in smell, into electrical energy that we call nerve impulses. Those impulses travel to the brain where "odor centers," "pain centers," "pleasure centers," or "visual centers" are stimulated and produce a sensation.

HEARING.   We hear sound when a vibrating object pushes air molecules into sound waves that vibrate between about 15 and 15,000 vibrations (hertz) a second. The waves are collected by our outer ear and channeled along the ear canal to a drumlike membrane called the eardrum. The eardrum starts to vibrate and passes the sound wave vibrations first to a set of three tiny bones and then into a fluid-filled canal. Tiny hairs in the canal are agitated and send signals along the auditory nerve to the brain, where we "hear" a sound of a certain loudness and pitch, from the thin squeak of a mouse to the boom of thunder. If you are wondering whether thunder makes a "noise" if no one is around to hear it, it doesn't. Thunder sets up a train of sound waves, but there is no "noise" until the waves enter an ear.

SIGHT.   Light-sensitive cells (the retina) located on the rear wall of the eyeball can detect light waves ranging from a frequency of about 4,000Å (violet) to about 7,000Å (red) (An angstrom [Å] is a very small unit of measure equal to 0.00000001 millimeter.) The sensory cells of the human retina that are called rods can detect shades of gray ranging from black to white. Other sensory cells, called cones, detect color. Depending on the frequency of the light waves striking the retina, the eye's sensory cells transmit a variety of electrical impulses to the optic nerve. The optic nerve then transmits those signals to brain centers where "sight" takes place.

TOUCH. Our bodies wear about six pounds of skin stretched out like pie dough to a thickness of a twentieth of an inch. The skin's millions of sensory cells continually inform us about whether an object is warm, cold, sharp, soft, rough, or smooth. The sensation of touch is more complex than either hearing or sight. When a farmer picks up a handful of soil to judge its quality, the sensory cells of his fingers and palm tell him whether the soil is fine or coarse, damp or dry, hard or soft. That mixture of information is provided by the skin's five basic sensitivities to pain, pressure, contact, cold, and heat.

SMELL. Smell and taste work together. Despite the nose's relatively poor development in humans, we can distinguish about 10,000 different odors, although many of the details of how we manage to do so are lacking. The sensory cells involved in odor detection are called chemoreceptors, and they need only a single molecule of the odorous substance to do their work. Attached to the roof of the nasal cavity is a one-square-inch patch of mucus-coated tissue with thousands of tiny hairs, which are extensions of nerve receptor cells. When we sniff the odor of baking bread, we cause currents of airborne bread molecules to come in contact with the nasal mucus and stimulate the nasal receptor cells within. The receptor cells detect and identify the chemical signal, convert it into an electrical signal, and send it along the olfactory nerve to the brain. The brain then tells us that we smell baking bread. Our ability to separate and identify the near limitless variety of odors that flood us day and night is more puzzling than understood.

TASTE. Scattered over the surface of your tongue are numerous taste buds, which are collections of fifty to sixty sense cells called taste receptors. As we chew our food, some of it is dissolved and mixed with saliva. The fluid washes over the tongue's taste buds and delivers chemical signals to the receptor cells. The receptor cells then change the signals into electrical impulses that are sent along nerves leading to the brain, where the sensation of taste takes place.

We catalog our sense of taste into four classes—bitter, salty, sour, and sweet. In order to identify a specific taste, we sometimes must smell or see what we are tasting. For example, a blindfolded person with a cold cannot taste the difference between grapefruit juice and orange juice. Also, what we expect a new food to taste like can affect whether we find the taste pleasant.

Our perceptual world can be temporarily overloaded with input signals; for example, an air traffic controller might be trying to monitor and instruct too many airplanes at once. In such situations chaos can result and bring on a temporary nervous breakdown. At the other extreme, deprivation of sensory input (solitary confinement for a long time, for example) can cause a different kind of breakdown. Starved of sensory input, the nervous system responds by inventing substitute artificial sensations called hallucinations.

During the course of evolution our sensory perception system has "learned" to recognize certain aspects of the environment and to ignore certain others. Information that is important to an earthworm's survival will not keep an eagle alive and well. Each species has its own unique sensory apparatus designed for its successful survival in its corner of the environment. No two species, and no two human beings, perceive and react to the world in exactly the same way.

HOW WE LEARN

Of all human behaviors, learning seems to be the most useful in helping us to survive. We begin to learn even before we are born. A fetus in the womb can learn to respond to pressure signals tapped on its mother's stomach. And an old dog can learn a new trick when motivated. However, the question of how we best learn is plagued by more disagreement than agreement. (One consequence: a lack of consensus within our public school system regarding the best way to teach children!)

Any stable change introduced into an organism's behavior as a result of experience can be termed learning. The flight behavior of a moth around a light at night, the courtship and mating behavior of geese, and the massive marches of army ants are examples of instinctive behavior programmed by the animals' genes. These animals do not need to learn the behaviors. Ants troop to the drum beat of their genetic code. They are born knowing what to do. But the more biologically complex an animal is, the less influence the role of instinct seems to have on its behavior. Among humans, a great deal of learning seems to be a result of mimicking what other people do. Watch an infant copy the actions of older children in a room. The widely varied and marvelous cultural diversity among humans the world over, and the transmission of culture from one generation to the next, are products of learning and of communicating what is learned to others.

Over the years psychologists and biologists, alone and together, have tried to discover the ways in which we learn. All students of learning agree that learning takes place when we respond to stimuli. Stimuli may be received in the form of light, odor, or sound. Or, the behavior of people we admire may act as stimuli and, like the infant in a room with older children, we will copy their behavior.

CLASSICAL CONDITIONING is a form of learning studied by the Russian psychologist Ivan P. Pavlov and others. Through this kind of learning we act in a certain way whenever we receive a certain stimulus. For example, Pavlov trained dogs to drool whenever he rang a bell. First he showed food to a hungry dog, which made the dog drool in expectation of eating. Each time the dog was shown food, it drooled. Next Pavlov rang a little bell each time he showed food to the dog. Eventually the dog learned to associate the ringing bell with food. After that the dog began to drool each time it heard the ringing bell, even though there was no food. A whistle, a touch, a flash of light, or any other stimulus that the dog's sensory apparatus can perceive can be substituted for a bell. As a method of learning, classical conditioning can be applied to humans and many other animals.

Many of us learn fear through conditioning. Consider this example: The mother of a small child goes into the yard and is horrified to find the child happily playing with a harmless grass snake. The child never has been taught to fear snakes, but the mother's fear brings a piercing shriek that startles and terrifies the child. Several times more the child hears the mother's terrified shriek as he fearlessly catches a snake. Eventually the child become conditioned by the mother's expression of fear of snakes and begins to shriek whenever he sees a snake. A fear of mice, spiders, bees, and certain other animals is commonly, although usually unknowingly, taught to children who become so conditioned that they rarely overcome the fear.

INSTRUMENTAL CONDITIONING   is a form of learning studied by B. F. Skinner. The following conversation describes how it works:

FATHER: Say a word, any word.
SON: Red.
FATHER: That's a good word. Say another word.
SON: Skates.
FATHER: Say another word.
   This exchange continues for many more words without the father again saying "That's a good word," until his son names another color quite by accident.
SON: Blue.
FATHER: That's a good word. Say another word.
SON: Sparkle.
FATHER: (silence)
SON: Green.
FATHER: That's a good word.
SON: Purple.
FATHER: That's a good word.

The son soon recognizes the pattern of the word game and from then on answers with a color every time his father says "Say another word." This form of learning is called instrumental conditioning. It differs from classical conditioning by the use of positive reinforcement ("That's a good word.").

Skinner used the following method to study instrumental conditioning. He placed a pigeon in a box and put some seeds on the floor of the box. Because pigeons peck as part of their food-getting behavior, the pigeon continued to peck at various parts of the box when all the seeds were gone. Skinner had installed a small wooden bar on one wall of the box. Every time the pigeon just happened to peck at the bar Skinner dropped a seed into the box through a small opening. Soon the pigeon had learned— through the use of positive reinforcement—that every time it pecked at the bar it received food. The boy learned that color words were wanted, and the pigeon quickly learned that pecks on the wooden bar were wanted, because there was always a reward; food for the pigeon and continuation of the game for the boy. I once saw a cartoon showing two pigeons in a Skinner box. One bird was saying to the other: "Boy, have I got him conditioned. Every time I peck at this bar he drops food to me."

Circus animals are taught complex tricks by careful positive reinforcement of certain responses. For example, a trainer can teach a pigeon to "dance" in a circle by reshaping the pigeon's pecking response into a turning response. (Many an infant, or child, trains its mother to pick it up or give it candy through *negative* reinforcement—crying until it gets its way!)

AUTONOMIC LEARNING (OR BIOFEEDBACK) first gained popularity in the 1950s and 1960s through the combined investigations of psychologists and physiologists. It is called "autonomic" learning because it involves the autonomic nervous system, the part of the nervous system that automatically regulates heartbeat, breathing rate, urine formation, and other bodily activities that are controlled without our having to think about them.

In the early experiments laboratory rats were taught to increase or decrease their heart rate, blood pressure, blood vessel diameter, and other "involuntary" body functions. The researchers observed normal cycles of changes (in heart rate, for example) over a period of time. Next, they rewarded the rat every time its heart rate automatically slowed, as expected through observation. The rat was rewarded because the wanted response occurred. They also punished the rat every time its heart rate automatically speeded up, as expected through observation. Before long the rat's heart regularly beat more slowly. In some way, the rat had learned to control its heart rate.

A number of clinical psychologists practice biofeedback and claim that they have taught their patients to lower their blood pressure or heart rate at will. It has been suggested that some of the amazing feats of certain practitioners of Yoga, such as walking barefoot over beds of hot coals without being burned, and of Sherpa porters going barefoot in the snow without freezing their feet, are the result of autonomic learning, or biofeedback.

However we learn, for the most part we tend to learn and accept those ideas that reinforce what we already know and believe, and we often reject ideas that contradict what we have been taught. The mark of an intelligent person is the ability to reorganize ideas, revise old beliefs, and dissolve recognized prejudices on the basis of new information that is integrated through learning.

HOW WE COMMUNICATE

WITH WORDS. Although the "language" of poetry, the "language" of science, and the "language" of national advertising draw from the same store of words, they involve us in quite different ways. Words color what we see, what we feel, what we hear. Words are windows through which we interpret the world. Words are also walls, sometimes preventing us from seeing something that is quite "obvious" to someone else. A word of praise from the right person at the right moment can set us up for the day; a word of criticism at the wrong moment can ruin the day. A word of pity, a word of scorn, a word of hope, an unspoken word . . . all color our lives.

The scientist and the poet use words quite differently, for each seeks a certain kind of truth, and the truths are not the same. The scientist uses words to describe, as accurately and unemotionally as possible, what is observed. The emotional effect the words may have on the reader are utterly unimportant to the scientist. The words are intended to be as impersonal and as free of emotion as the square root of nine.

The same cannot be said of poets, who use words not to inform but to evoke responses in us by moving us emotionally or opening in us new

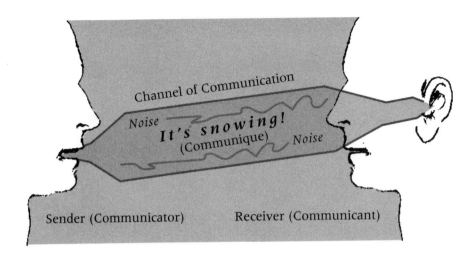

Channel of Communication

Noise

It's snowing!
(Communique)

Noise

Sender (Communicator)   Receiver (Communicant)

A communication system is made up of a communicator; a communique; a channel of communication; the likelihood of noise, or interference in the channel; and a communicant. In the diagram the communicator is a person, the communique is "It's snowing!", the channel is a telephone line, noise in the channel is static on the line that distorts the communique, and the communicant is another person. Using this model, describe a communication system in which the communicator is an artificial satellite.

awarenesses. Often a poet re-creates an experience of his own and tries to involve us in it, tries to get us to respond to it.

If you put a red filter over the lens of a camera, the filter stops all visible light except that of red. When you look through the camera, you view a rose-colored world, but your experience tells you that the world is not really rose-colored. But perhaps it is—to some creature whose eyes admit only red light. To say that the world out there is *really* like this or that is impossible. We perceive it through the filters of our eyes, ears, fingers, and the special sensing devices that we can build in the laboratory. But what is kept out by those filters cannot be known to us directly; and what is distorted by them can be only imperfectly known.

Languages also are filters, causing us to feel certain ways about the world and to react to the world in certain ways. Unfortunately, few of us can change "language filters" and feel the world as a speaker of Aivilik, Hopi, or Japanese feels it. As the language scholar S. I. Hayakawa said, the world out there, the *objective world*, is an intensely personal relationship between you and it.

> How many different ways can you say "ah"?
> • As a group of children on first seeing a puppy.
> • As a girl seeing a mouse.
> • As someone who just got rid of a very boring person.
> • As a workman who just bashed his thumb with a hammer.

Like individual words or sounds, language can be viewed in several contexts. It provides a limitless assortment of words that give meaning to what we perceive through our senses. It enables us to frame the laws that regulate our society. It also enables us to frame the personal values that give us a "philosophy of life." Language often gives order to our emotions and serves as a control that prevents us from losing command. And language enables us to store information and the accumulated knowledge gained since writing was invented some 5,000 or more years ago.

WITHOUT WORDS. The term "body language" refers to communication that does not involve spoken language. In addition, of course, blind people have a touch sign language to communicate with each other, and deaf people use their hands in a visual sign language. Some of our nonverbal communication skills, such as sign languages, are learned, and some are inborn, or instinctive.

Anthropologists who have studied facial expressions in many different cultures conclude that a smile is a smile the world around. A frown indicates discontent. Raised eyebrow flashes are a sign of flirtation, and so on with certain other facial expressions. The fact that such expressions are universally used and understood is proof that they are as instinctive as a dog's growl or a baby's cry.

All of us add to our collection of instinctive body language as we develop a "vocabulary" of learned body twists, shrugs, nods, and other motions.

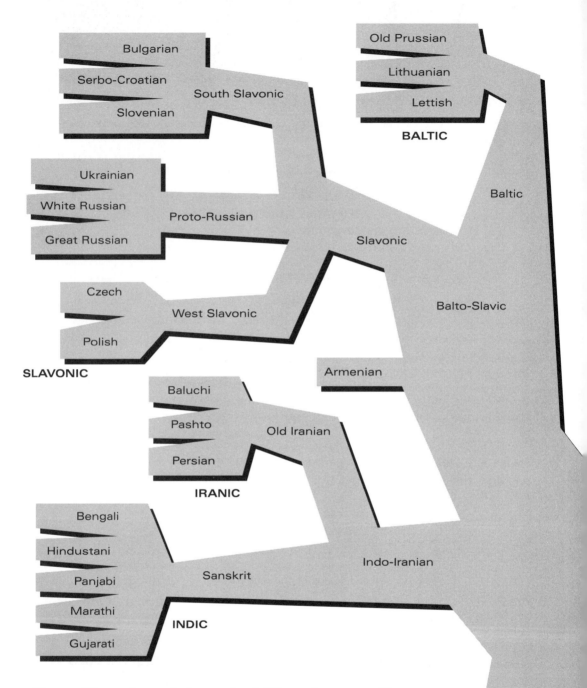

Bulgarian
Serbo-Croatian
Slovenian
South Slavonic

Old Prussian
Lithuanian
Lettish
BALTIC

Ukrainian
White Russian
Great Russian
Proto-Russian

Baltic

Slavonic

Czech
Polish
West Slavonic

Balto-Slavic

SLAVONIC

Armenian

Baluchi
Pashto
Persian
Old Iranian

IRANIC

Bengali
Hindustani
Panjabi
Marathi
Gujarati
Sanskrit

Indo-Iranian

INDIC

Eastern
Indo-European

IN

The world's people speak thousands of different languages. There are more than one thousand Native American languages and about the same number of African languages. People in New Guinea speak about 700 languages, in the former Soviet Union, about 130. Chinese is the world's most widely spoken language. Some time around 3000 B.C., a people called the Indo-Europeans settled far and wide over Europe and

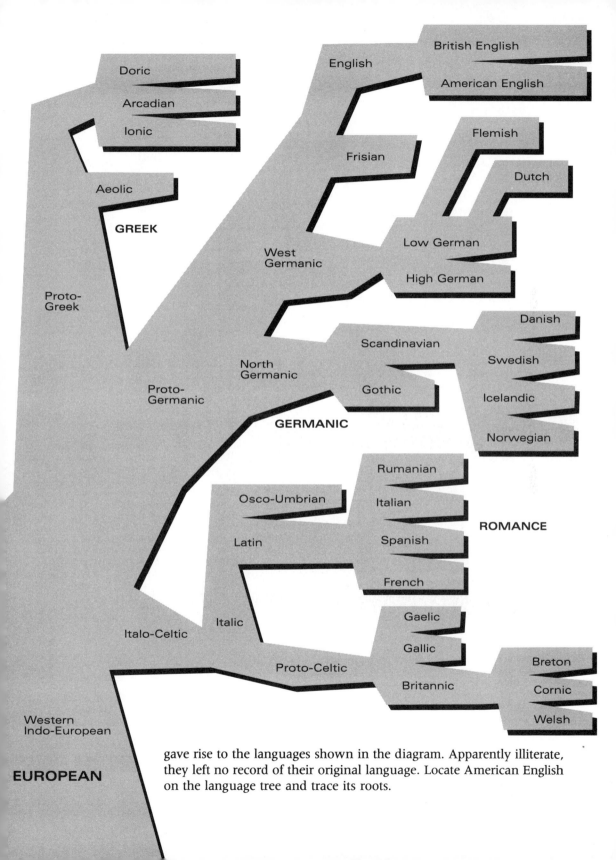

gave rise to the languages shown in the diagram. Apparently illiterate, they left no record of their original language. Locate American English on the language tree and trace its roots.

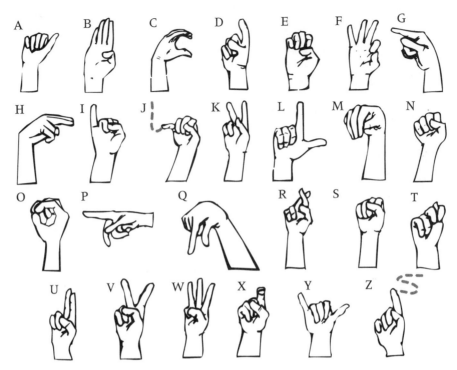

Signing is a silent hand language used by the deaf. It is possible to spell out the words of a sentence letter-by-letter (the American Sign Language alphabet is shown here), but it is faster to use the large store of signs in which a given sign, or combination of signs, denotes an act or object or condition. For example, to express hunger you would place your flattened hand on your stomach and move your hand in a continuous circle two or three times.

In the Western world we are taught to move our head up and down to signal yes and side to side to mean no. But certain groups in India do just the opposite.

Each of us, it seems, has a sense of ownership of the space around us. "Please knock before you enter *my* room," you might warn. In school, if someone's book bag topples too close to "your space" you may unobtrusively push it away with your foot. Such actions are expressions of territory ownership and may be accompanied by body language of some sort.

The sneakers and jeans we wear, the hair style we choose, and the way we walk are all examples of body language that say something about us. Deliberately avoiding eye contact with another person can indicate fear, hostility, or intentional indifference. A quick, nervous smile from a person who accidentally bumps into someone can be an unspoken apology. A long stare with tightened eyes usually means hostility. Women learn to sit in a certain way to avoid expressing their sexuality, especially when they wear very short skirts. But in the next moment they may move a certain way in order to attract attention by expressing their sexuality. We wear party faces, classroom faces, funeral faces. All are body language masks designed to display the way we think we *should* feel at the moment.

Body language and spoken language work together to strengthen or amplify a message. We take a course in public speaking to learn how to use certain gestures to emphasize the spoken word and so help make a point. As we speak with intensity with someone, we raise an eyebrow, bite our lip, wave a hand, stomp a foot, rub our nose, blink our eyes. Each gesture is intuitively orchestrated with our spoken words, and the two merge as a single message, one reinforcing the other.

According to one psychological study of body language, "The difference between maturity and immaturity is often telegraphed by body language. Too much body movement without real meaning is immature. A mature person moves when he has to, and moves purposefully."

INTELLIGENCE

Is human intelligence inherited, or is it learned? Or maybe a bit of each? The acquisition of intelligence is one of the most emotionally loaded debates about human behavior in and out of science. (And the debate involves questions about how we can best test intelligence.)

One problem in addressing the issue is that we don't have a good working definition of intelligence. Generally, it refers to all-encompassing effectiveness of a person's mental processes, especially comprehension, learning ability, memory, thinking, and reasoning ability. This vague description makes it difficult to identify specific aspects of intelligence that can be tested. But some areas suitable for testing have been identified. They include the ability to: (1) use language as a tool for understanding, (2) work with numbers, (3) visualize objects arranged in space, (4) remember, and (5) reason through a problem. Intelligence, then, consists of a number of overlapping skills and is not a single, well-defined capability.

Identical twins have the same genetic makeup. Therefore, we might expect them to be equally intelligent, and intelligence tests given to identical twins reared in the same social environment confirm that expectation. Interestingly, however, studies of identical twins reared in different social environments show a difference in intelligence scores. A twin reared in a rich social environment scores higher than her counterpart reared in an impoverished social environment. Other studies show that an intelligence score can be raised if a child is transferred from an impoverished social environment to one rich with pleasant social stimuli.

Among the most widely used intelligence tests are the Stanford-Binet tests (named after the French psychologist Alfred Binet who first developed them in 1908). The tests consist of short tasks, given by a tester who presents questions to the person being tested. The individual's score, or IQ (Intelligence Quotient), considers two things: the mental age level of ability, determined by tasks correctly performed, compared with the actual age of the individual.

It isn't until about age five that children begin to show significant differences in scores that suggest a low, medium, or high level of intelligence later as an adult. After about age twelve the tests provide a fairly reliable forecast of the child's future intelligence. Because large changes in IQ are possible as a child grows older, it is unwise to use an IQ score as the *only* indicator of a child's intellectual progress over the years. Only people trained in measuring intelligence should do so, and they always take into consideration a number of conditions that might affect a child's mental progress, such as the child's home environment and the quality of instruction available.

Despite disagreements over the value and fairness of IQ tests, job success later in life is fairly consistent with IQ scores. The average IQ of people who become physicists, college professors, and business managers, for example, is consistently higher than the average IQ of those who become laborers in unskilled jobs that require relatively less intelligence.

Even so, intelligence tests have come under fire over the past several years. Some critics say that the tests' measure of intelligence relies too much on verbal skills and so discriminates against the poor. Verbal skills, they argue, reflect the type of upbringing, social background, and education a family is willing and able to provide. In other words, a low IQ score may relflect an "imperfect" home environment rather than "imperfect" genes.

Other critics charge that IQ tests have become instruments for discriminating against the lower social classes and minorities. That claim becomes increasingly harder to defend as IQ tests are regularly improved to weed out items of cultural bias.

Apparently it is easier to identify factors that encourage a higher IQ than to identify what discourages one. Psychologists of all schools of intelligence testing agree that mothers can enhance their children's intelligence by playing with, talking to, reading to, and otherwise interacting with their babies. The mother's health while she carries her baby for those nine months is also extremely important, as is seeing that her children are provided with a healthful diet as they grow.

SOCIAL CHANGE

No matter how small a social unit may be (a family) or how large (a nation or partnership of nations), one thing is inescapable: conflict. And each social unit, whether a clan, a club, a political party, or a religious group, has methods of dealing with conflict, at least most of the time. Sometimes those methods are unspoken rules that are understood and respected on the family level. Or they may take the form of written laws, such as a club's bylaws or highway speed limits. Or they may be age-old behavioral guides such as the Ten Commandments.

When we disobey, meaning that we choose not to conform to the rules on any level of society, we risk punishment because society looks on the nonconformist as a threat to order and its well-being. This is as true in a colony of honeybees or in a troop of baboons as it is in a socially troubled city or the jungles of the Congo. In human society, punishment can range from temporary isolation ("Go to your room and stay there!") to arrest and imprisonment for life, torture, or execution. Sometimes political conflict within a nation divides its citizens into two camps of opposing beliefs and leads to civil war, as occurred over the issue of slavery in the United States in the mid-1800s. War is the severest and most destructive form of punishment. But like punishment of a much milder nature, it is sometimes necessary if the values of society are to be upheld for the common good.

Conflict is at the basis of virtually all social change—conflict brought about by opposing ideals, differences in living standards among groups or nations, racial and other forms of prejudice, or new technology that threatens to upset the established economic or social order of the day. Those in favor of the change are the ones most likely to benefit. Those who oppose the change feel threatened.

The world in the 1990s is very different from what it was in 1925. Increased population growth coupled with modern communication technologies have made the world a smaller place, prone to more rapid and more drastic change—and opportunities for conflict—than ever before. Today we are members of a global community, which means that many of our values and group behaviors eventually will have to be tailored accordingly. A change in one or more oil-producing nations of the Persian Gulf can affect the world economy overnight. Today the wealth, security, and general welfare of almost all nations are interrelated. If disaster by nuclear weapons or the economic strangulation of many are to be avoided, all nations must soon learn to behave as a global society, not as individual states living in isolation. And each of us, as individuals, must learn to feel ourselves as members of that global society.

Six

THE PHYSICAL WORLD

THE "BIG BANG" BIRTH OF THE UNIVERSE

It must have been the most fantastic explosion anyone can imagine. What was to become every piece of matter and every bit of energy in the Universe was packed into a tiny cosmic super-atom. Sometime between twelve and twenty billion years ago that super-atom exploded in what astronomers call the Big Bang, and time and the Universe began. The fireball explosion of the Big Bang sent energy rushing off in all directions. At that moment the Universe began to grow larger, and it has been expanding ever since. At least that's what our telescopes seem to show us today.

Just after the explosion, nearly all of the Universe was a hot cloud of hydrogen. Over the next several seconds, some of the hydrogen fused and formed helium, just as happens today in the hot core of the Sun and other stars. Then over the next minute or so, as the young Universe kept expanding, the hydrogen was spread out too thinly for more fusions to take place. Only a few minutes after the Universe began, nine tenths of the atoms in it were hydrogen and one tenth had become helium.

GALAXIES FORM

From about a hundred thousand to a million years after the Big Bang, the hydrogen and helium gases had collected into giant clouds. Those clouds were the early states of the countless galaxies—the vast cities of stars we observe throughout space. In the early stages of the galaxies we can imagine that some parts of a galaxy cloud had large and dense collections of hydrogen

Galaxies galore stretch away into space as far as telescopes can see. The galaxy seen edge-on is one designated M104 and is seen in the constellation Virgo. The spiral galaxy seen from a top view and designated M81 can be seen in the constellation the Big Dipper. It probably resembles our own galaxy. (*Hale Observatories*)

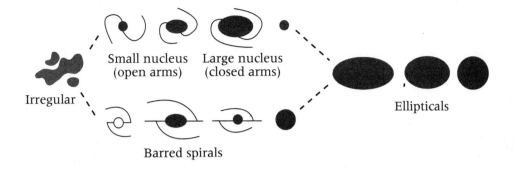

Irregular
Small nucleus (open arms)
Large nucleus (closed arms)
Ellipticals
Barred spirals

We can arrange galaxies in a sequence of forms. The irregular galaxies, at one end of the sequence, are rich in young stars. But they also contain old objects. Next come the spiral galaxies with small centers and loosely wound arms. Next come galaxies with larger centers and more tightly wound spiral arms and fewer youthful stars. At the far end of the sequence are the elliptical galaxies, which are made up almost entirely of old stars. Astronomers do not agree about how the shape of a galaxy might be related to its age, or if there is any relation at all.

and helium and other parts had only small amounts. Today our giant telescopes show us billions of galaxies. All seem to be about ten billion to fifteen billion years old, more than twice the age of our local star, the Sun.

The galaxies are enormous wheeling collections of hundreds of billions of stars. Some, such as Andromeda and our home galaxy, the Milky Way, are shaped like enormous spinning spirals. Some spirals have tightly wrapped arms; in others the arms are loosely wrapped. Some spirals have bars running through their centers and are called barred-spirals. There also are elliptical galaxies, some shaped like a football, others like a sphere. There are irregular galaxies, such as the Milky Way's two companion galaxies called the Magellanic Clouds, which lack a definite shape. And there are peculiar galaxies, each of which has some oddity, such as an exploding central region.

Most galaxies are arranged in large groups called clusters. Our Local Group cluster contains about twenty-one galaxies, more than half of which are elliptical. The Local Group has a diameter of about three million light-years. (One light-year is the distance light travels in one year at the rate of

186,000 miles a second, which amounts to about six trillion miles.) Clusters of galaxies stretch off into space for as far as we can see with telescopes. Within 50 million light-years of us are many dozens similar in size to our Local Group.

Clusters of galaxies form superclusters. One supercluster in the constellation Hercules is thought to be 350 million light-years across. Possibly the system of clusters and superclusters continues into super-superclusters. Our current knowledge indicates that our lumpy Universe of galaxy clusters stretches off in every direction for at least ten billion light-years.

THE EXPANDING UNIVERSE

No matter which direction we look in space we see countless billions of galaxies all rushing away from us, as if we were motionless at the center of the Universe. But a person on any one of those galaxies would see the same rushing-away motion. The more distant a galaxy, the greater its rushing-away speed. From all we can observe, the Universe seems to have been expanding ever since the Big Bang. Will it go on expanding forever, or will something stop it? If the Universe has enough matter, gravity will slow down the expansion and reverse it, just as Earth's gravity slows down and reverses the motion of a ball you toss into the air. Eventually the galaxies may slow down, stop and hang motionless for a cosmic instant, and then begin to fall inward. If that happens, all matter will tumble together again in the Big Squeeze billions of years from now. The Big Squeeze may then form another cosmic egg that will explode in another Big Bang and start the process all over again. If so, we may be living in a born-again Universe. This is the oscillating model of the Universe, which some astronomers call the Bang-Bang-Bang theory.

One argument against the oscillating Universe theory is that there may not be enough mass in the Universe to slow its expansion. If so, we may be living in a Universe that will expand away forever and simply run down, never to be reborn.

STARS FORM

Stars are immense globes of extremely hot gases that emit radiant energy all along the electromagnetic spectrum. They form from dense clouds of gas and cosmic dust within the galaxies. The clouds are about 90 percent hydrogen gas and about 10 percent helium and have scattered molecules of heavier solid particles. As a star cloud collapses in on itself under the influence of gravitation, its matter is compressed and heats. At first, a young star cloud, called a protostar, glows a dull red from the heat produced in its core. As the core temperature reaches ten million kelvins (degrees) or higher, the young star begins to fuse hydrogen into helium. This new source of energy causes a star like the Sun to shine with a hotter yellowish-white light. More massive stars become hotter and shine with a bluish-white light. The least massive dwarf stars are relatively cool and shine with a reddish light. Color, then, is an important clue to a star's character.

After billions of years, a star exhausts the hydrogen fuel supply in its core. It then collapses in on itself, heats explosively for a brief time, and then swells as a red giant star. As a red giant, the star briefly resists collapse by using helium to fuel new nuclear reactions, forming carbon. Eventually, the helium, too, is exhausted. A very massive star may repeat this process several times, using the product from one stage of reactions as fuel for the next stage, forming carbon, then oxygen, magnesium, and silicon and so on up to iron. Finally, though, all available fuel is gone. Without energy output from the core, the star once again collapses, but this time it keeps on shrinking, ending its life first as a white dwarf star, then finally as a cold dark object called a black dwarf.

The final collapse of *very* massive stars produces catastrophic explosions called supernovas. The heavy matter cast off from a supernova crosses space and mixes with clouds of the lighter elements hydrogen and helium and so enriches them with heavy elements. The Sun and its nine known planets were formed out of just such an enriched cloud. The remains of a supernova star's dense core may undergo further collapse and become a neutron star, or a strange object called a black hole. The matter composing a black hole is so dense and its gravitation so strong that nothing can escape from it, not even light.

Under the influence of gravitation and nuclear fusions, matter is continually transformed into energy in the cores of stars, as it has been for billions of years and as it will continue to be for billions more.

OUR SOLAR SYSTEM HOME

As stars form out of immense clouds of gas and dust, so planets form out of the gas and dust cloud of their parent star. Planets are relatively cool, small objects that revolve about a star that gravitationally holds them captive in nearly circular orbits (actually ellipses) around the star. Our Solar System home consists of one star (the Sun), nine known planets with a total of more than fifty moons, millions of comets, and billions of rock-metal fragments called meteoroids.

Some five billion years ago the Sun was a cool globe of gas rotating at the center of a spinning disk of mostly hydrogen and helium mixed with smaller amounts of carbon, silicates, iron, and other heavy elements. Tiny dust grains within the disk matter collided and began clumping together. Clumps attracted other clumps until the disk contained many billions of solid objects, called planetesimals, ranging from a few centimeters to many meters in size. Some were ices, others were rocky matter, and still others were a mix of rock and metal. The more massive clumps gravitationally swept up less massive ones, and the nine known planets were formed by a process called accretion. As the planets were forming by accretion, so were their moons also forming by accretion, except for some that seem to be captured asteroids.

Out at the distance of Jupiter and beyond, temperatures were much lower and volatile materials like methane and ammonia were able to condense into the planetesimals. Thus there were more and larger planetesimals in this region and they built up into very large planets. In addition, the tidal

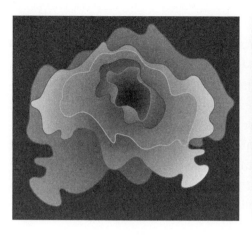 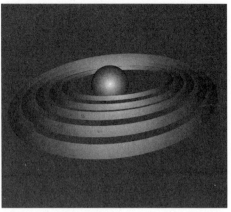

FORMATION OF THE SOLAR SYSTEM

1. Some 4.6 billion years ago a massive cloud of mostly hydrogen, some helium, and lesser amounts of heavier elements, gravitationally collapses in on itself.

2. The central region becomes dense and heats up as the proto-Sun. Clumps of matter form in the whirling disk region, the more massive clumps (the proto-planets) sweeping up the less massive ones.

3. Eventually, space between the planets is swept clean, except for the many asteroids orbiting between Mars and Jupiter, and comets that periodically sweep in from the outer edge of the Solar System.

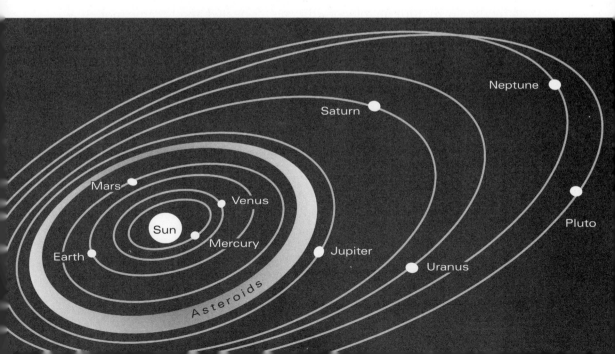

effects of the Sun's gravity were much less at this distance, and this also encouraged the accretion of planetesimals into large objects. This may help explain why the outer planets (Jupiter, Saturn, Uranus, and Neptune) are large compared with the smaller inner planets (Mercury, Venus, Earth, and Mars). Unlike the less massive inner planets, the more massive and gravitationally powerful outer planets attracted and held onto large amounts of disk gases, including hydrogen, methane, and ammonia. Again, the lower temperatures made it easier to trap these light gases. These gases make up the bulk of the outer planets' atmospheres today, but are not present in the atmospheres of Venus, Earth, or Mars.

It seems almost certain that planets are by-products of star formation. And we, along with planet Earth, are made up of the chemical elements of the original solar disk cloud. We are the product of star formation.

EARTH'S STRUCTURE AND COMPOSITION

About 4.6 billion years ago Earth was a soupy ball of molten rock and metals at a temperature of about 2,000°C (3,600°F). The planets formed as clumps of rocky and metallic matter that were spread out around the Sun came together into globes of material. As surrounding matter was swept up by the newly forming planets, the matter heated and became molten as it compacted ever more densely in the new planets' core regions.

As the molten rock and metal materials shifted about within Earth, the heavier matter sank into the core region. Such materials included the heavy metals iron and nickel. At the same time, lighter matter floated up to the surface. Such materials were mostly lightweight silicate rock such as we find today at the surface. Gradually the surface cooled and solidified.

Today, Earth is like a set of nesting globes. One, an eggshell-thin crust of solid rock, is about 9.6 kilometers (6 miles) thick beneath the oceans and about 60 kilometers (37 miles) thick beneath the continents. Most of the continents are made up of a granite-type rock. Temperatures within the crust may range up to about 980°C (1,800°F).

Beneath the crust is a much deeper layer called the mantle, which extends down about 2,900 kilometers (1,800 miles). The mantle is made up of rock that contains a lot of iron and magnesium. Because the mantle rock is under more pressure than the crustal rock, it is hotter. Its matter may be squeezed this way and that like toothpaste in a tube. The temperature of the mantle may range from about 500°C (950°F) to 4,150°C (7,500°F).

The core seems to be a large ball of solid iron and nickel surrounded by a layer of liquid iron and nickel. It's depth ranges from about 2,900 kilometers (1,800 miles) to 6,360 kilometers (3,950 miles), which marks Earth's center. The temperature there may be about 4,000°C (7,000°F). Earth's interior is heated by the energy released by the decay of radioactive materials in it.

ROCKS AND MINERALS

If you took a rock apart and had a way of examining it closely, you would find that it is made up of bits and pieces of different kinds of minerals. Minerals are solid elements or compounds found free in nature. Examples include copper, gold, quartz, carbon, salt, and silver. Minerals are the building blocks of rocks. Although the rocks around us seem ageless, they are not. Rocks are worn away by wind, rain, and frost, broken into tiny grains, and carried by streams and rivers into lakes and the seas where they carpet the lake or sea floor with fine pieces of themselves called sediments. Century after century the loose sediments pile up, all the while squeezed by the great weight of new sediments drifting down from above. This squeezing process, combined with other forces, causes the sediments to harden into new rock.

Whereas the sediments harden to rock, rock in turn can be changed by forces within Earth's crust. It can be melted, twisted, or folded, and gradually changed into a different kind of rock. The new rock can then be pushed up as a mountain range, where the process of wearing away begins anew. There are three major kinds of rocks.

IGNEOUS ROCK ("fire rock") is formed when liquid rock—magma—flows out of a volcano or up through cracks in the sea floor and hardens. At other times magma forms huge blisters that solidify just below the surface crustal rock. Or magma may melt its way between layers of solid rock and later harden. Such igneous rock formations are called batholiths, laccoliths, dikes, and sills, depending on their mass (batholiths and laccoliths), or whether they intrude their way horizontally between solid rock layers (sills), or whether they intrude their way vertically through solid rock layers (dikes). All are intrusive igneous rock because the magma "intrudes" into other rock. Lava is magma that hardens on top of the ground and is called extrusive igneous rock. Granite, obsidian, and basalt are examples of igneous rock.

SEDIMENTARY ROCK, common at Earth's surface, is made of bits and pieces of worn-away parts of other kinds of rock, and it often contains fossils, which are the remains of once-living things. Mud, lime, sand, and clay, all soft to the touch, were once part of solid rock and will be once again millions of years from now. The sediments that are washed down a mountainside and spread out as a giant fan at the mountain's base are deposited in layers season after season, year after year, century after century. Eventually they harden like a petrified layer cake, and they can easily be broken apart layer by layer. Shale, sandstone, limestone, and coal are examples of sedimentary rocks.

METAMORPHIC ROCK is formed about six miles or so within Earth's crust. The heat and pressure are so great there that igneous and sedimentary rock at that depth are not solid but plastic, meaning that they can be bent, folded, squeezed, and stretched into any shape. Also, the high pressure and heat change the very substance of the original rock, altering the minerals. When this "remade" rock is thrust up to the surface, it is called metamorphic rock. This remade rock also is formed at the contact zone where magma intrudes into existing solid rock and melts it. Marble is formed by the melting action of igneous rock. Slate is formed by a combination of pressure and heat.

Igneous rocks make up about 65 percent of Earth's crust, metamorphic rocks about 27 percent, and sedimentary rocks about 8 percent. The most plentiful minerals are quartz and feldspar, which make up 63 percent of the crustal rock.

TELLING GEOLOGIC TIME

According to geologists and biologists, Earth's age and long history of life go back thousands of millions of years. But how do we know this for a fact? According to fundamentalist Christians, Earth is only about 10,000 years old.

Around the year 1900, scientists discovered that uranium and other radioactive elements decay at a predictable rate. As they decay, they change into different elements—uranium decays into lead, potassium decays into argon, and so on. Scientists can date a sample of rock by using the known decay rate of an element such as uranium, which changes into lead. For example, they can compare the number of unchanged uranium atoms with the number of atoms that have decayed into lead.

The amount of time required for half of the atoms of a radioactive element to decay is called the element's "half-life." Nothing seems to affect the half-life of any radioactive element, not even the forces of heat or pressure. Because scientists know the half-life of the radioactive element, and because the number of new (lead) atoms can be compared to the number of old (uranium) atoms, it is a simple matter to tell how long the radioactive "clock" has been ticking. Different radioactive elements have different half-lives. Uranium–238, for example, decays to lead–206 in 4,510 million years. Because different radioactive elements have different decay rates, they can be used as clocks to measure different lengths of time.

Geological clocks have given us a reliable way to estimate the age of a rock at 150 million years or another at only 30 million years. And any fossil contained in a 150-million-year-old rock must also be around 150 million years old, because the animal or plant became fossilized when the rock was being formed.

The discovery of radioactive dating made it possible to date many events in Earth's long history. For instance, the oldest known Earth rocks have an age of 3.96 billion years. The oldest known Moon rocks are from 4.5 to 4.6 billion years old. The oldest known land animals have an age of 414 million years. It is on the basis of radioactive dating that we estimate the age of the Solar System at a few hundred million years more than about 4.6 billion years.

EARTH'S NATURAL RESOURCES

As the world population continues to grow at its fastest rate ever, we find it necessary to draw on the planet's natural resources at an increasing rate to meet our demands for energy and materials. There are two classes of natural resources: those that are renewable and those that are not renewable.

We must ask ourselves two questions: (1) Is uncontrolled industrial growth consuming many of the planet's renewable resources faster than nature can renew them? and (2) How much longer can the nonrenewable resources be economically recoverable at the rates of consumption anticipated over the next century or more?

Renewable resources include land, water, marshlands, forests, and the other plants and animals with which we share Earth's ecosystems. The world's tropical rain forests and marshlands are among the most biologically productive ecosystems on the planet, but the hunger for raw materials coupled with development are rapidly destroying both. Half of the world's tropical rain forests have been destroyed already, and experts expect the remaining half to be gone within 50 years.

In the past 150 years, 25 to 50 percent of the world's marshlands have been destroyed. Not too long ago America's grasslands supported millions of bison, elk, and antelope. Virtually all are now gone, and the animals living on Africa's grasslands are meeting the same fate. Used in moderation, renewable natural resources could be stabilized. But the growing population's appetite for those resources gradually erodes them away. How can we conserve what is left for present needs and for the needs of future generations?

Many nonrenewable resources—fossil fuels (coal, oil, and natural gas) and metals—are being devoured as rapidly as renewable ones. These resources are said to be "nonrenewable" because the geologic processes that form them take thousands or millions of years. Industry gobbles up the planet's nonrenewable resources at an ever increasing rate. Since 1900 aluminum production has increased 1,700-fold, petroleum production 125-fold, steel production 70-fold, and coal production 7-fold.

If we ask whether we are in danger of running out of the stores of copper, aluminum, coal, and other resources locked up in Earth's crustal rock, the answer probably is no, with a few exceptions. But asking whether we can keep digging or pumping those resources out of the ground at an ever increasing rate over the next century or more at an affordable cost is a different question. The deeper we have to dig or drill for a resource, the more expensive it becomes to remove it. When the cost of mining a resource such as copper becomes more than people can afford to pay for the copper, we have *effectively* run out of that resource. At present, however, it appears that a number of "important" metals, including iron, aluminum, and manganese, exist in adequate supply at a manageable cost for many years to come.

CONTINENTS THAT WANDER

Ever since Earth developed a solid rock crust more than four billion years ago, the continents have been wandering about. Continental drift and plate tectonics are the terms geologists use to describe Earth's crustal restlessness.

Among the first evidence that the continents break apart and rejoin was the 1912 observation of German geologist Alfred Wegener that the coastlines of western Africa and eastern South America fit neatly together like pieces of a jigsaw puzzle. He also pointed out that the rocks and fossils on opposite shores of the Atlantic Ocean were so alike that the two shores must have been joined in the distant past. More recently scientists have shown that many undersea mountain ridges form a continuous global chain some 64,000 kilometers (40,000 miles) long. Hundreds of miles wide in some places, the chain snakes its way around the globe and sometimes pokes mountain peaks above sea level. Such peaks include Easter Island, the Azores, and the Hawaiian Islands.

Along the ridge top of the mountain chain is a rift valley. From time to time molten rock from the hot mantle beneath wells up through a "hot spot," cools, and forms new crust. As it does, it spreads the sea floor out on both sides of the ridge. Spreading of the sea floor in the Atlantic basin occurs at the rate of about an inch a year.

The continents are lightweight rafts of silicate rock floating in a puttylike sea of heavyweight basaltic rock of the upper mantle. Called plates, the rafts come in two sizes—six major ones and about a dozen smaller ones. Wherever the edges of two plates grind together there is an earthquake zone. When two plates collide there is major geological activity. For example, spreading of the Atlantic sea floor is pushing the Nazca plate eastward against the South American plate along the coasts of Chile and Peru. Meanwhile, the South American plate is being pushed westward, also by sea floor spreading. The lightweight continental rock of the South American plate rides up over the heavyweight basaltic rock of the Nazca plate. The forward-moving edge of the Nazca plate is pushed down into the hot mantle rock under the edge of the South American plate. The heat of the mantle rock then melts the leading edge of the Nazca plate. This newly melted rock next forces its way up through the South American plate. Then the fluid rock from time to time boils up to the surface and spills over the surrounding land as volcanic eruption.

As mountain ranges such as the mighty Andes are thrust up by plate collisions, deep ocean trenches are formed. The Pacific Ocean has several— the Aleutian Trench, the Japan Trench, and the Marianas Trench. All are about 9.6 kilometers (6 miles) deep. As a plate slides over a hot spot in the mantle, a train of mountain peaks is continuously popped up. The Hawaiian

Islands are a result of such hot-spot mountain formation. The most recent end of the chain is the youngest link and is represented by the island of Hawaii, which is only about two million years old. The oldest link is at the other end and is represented by the Midway group of islands, which are about twenty-five million years old.

THE OCEANS

The oceans, which cover 70.8 percent of Earth's surface, are the ultimate collecting grounds for the millions of tons of mud, clay, sand, and other sediments that are continuously washed off the continents by streams and rivers. They also are the collecting grounds for many of the pollutants we generate—oil spilled accidentally, garbage, toxic chemicals, and radioactive wastes.

The oceans were formed some four billion or so years ago as Earth's hot surface rocks underwent cooling. Volcanoes and great crustal cracks were still issuing many gases into the air, including water vapor, carbon dioxide, carbon monoxide, and methane. As the water vapor rose into the cold upper air, it cooled, changed into liquid water, and fell to the surface as rain. But most of the rocky crust was not yet cool enough for the rain to collect in pools. As torrents of water poured down on the hot rock, the water instantly hissed skyward as clouds of steam. The steam condensed again as rain, fell, and once again was cast skyward as water vapor.

Storm clouds must have blanketed Earth for thousands of years before the surface cooled enough to allow liquid water to collect in pools and flow as streams and rivers. As great rock basins gradually filled, the first seas were formed. And as streams and rivers continued to wash over the land, they picked up, dissolved, and carried salts and sediments with them. Eventually, after how many dark centuries we do not know, the great rains stopped. Dim light began shining through the thinning clouds, and one day the Sun's rays broke through, lighting for the first time a planet of jagged rock and sparkling blue water. Although much of Earth's water was produced by the process described above, much of it was also collected from comets that rained down onto the planet during its early centuries.

As salts and other minerals and soil particles are washed into the sea, they coat the broad underwater platform edges of the continents called the continental shelves. The shelves slope seaward from a few miles to more than 160 kilometers (100 miles). Their depths are not much more than

The oceans' surface currents serve as a global conveyor belt that moves huge amounts of heat from one place to another. One example is the Gulf Stream. It is a "river" of warm water that flows out of the Gulf of Mexico and across the Atlantic to Europe in a northeasterly direction. Its warm water provides Iceland, Britain, and parts of Scandinavia with a moderate climate. This map of the Gulf Stream was drawn by Benjamin Franklin. Arrows have been added to show how the Gulf Stream has changed course from time to time since the year 1550.

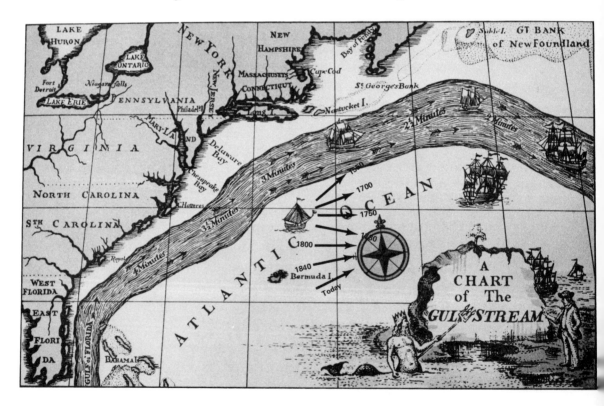

about 180 meters (600 feet). From time to time great collections of sediments poised at the edge of a section of continental shelf break loose and rush down the slope and far out onto the sea floor as a turbidity current. Additional sea floor materials come from the microscopic skeletons (silica and calcium carbonate) of tiny animals called plankton that continuously rain down onto the sea floor. Beneath the oceans' carpet of sediments is basaltic bedrock about 9.6 kilometers (6 miles) deep over the hot mantle rock.

Salts washed off the land give the sea its salty taste. The most common mineral salt is sodium chloride, common table salt. But there are other minerals, including magnesium, sulfur, calcium, and potassium. The hot Sun evaporates the surface water of the oceans and turns it into the dry gas water vapor. The salts and other minerals are left behind. The water vapor rises, cools, and falls over the land as rain, and so the water cycle continues endlessly. There are other such biogeochemical cycles—one that cycles carbon, one for nitrogen, one for oxygen, one for phosphorus, and so on.

An elaborate global pattern of surface ocean currents and deep-water currents keeps the oceans well-mixed; consequently their mineral composition has changed little over millions of years.

The sea floor has numerous topographical features, including mountain ranges, vast lifeless basins, deep trenches, isolated subsurface flat-top peaks call guyots, and coral reefs. The coral reefs are the world's richest ecosystems.

OCEAN TIDES. Twice each day we have a high tide and a low tide. The tides are caused by gravitational attraction of the Moon and Sun. The tides occur because the force of gravity becomes weaker with increasing distance. The oceans on the side of Earth nearest the Moon are closer to the Moon than is the sea floor beneath the water, hence gravity pulls more strongly on the water than on solid floor beneath. This causes the water to bulge up toward the Moon. On the opposite side of Earth, the oceans are farther from the Moon than is solid floor. Here the Moon's gravity pulls more strongly on solid floor than on the ocean water, in effect pulling Earth "out

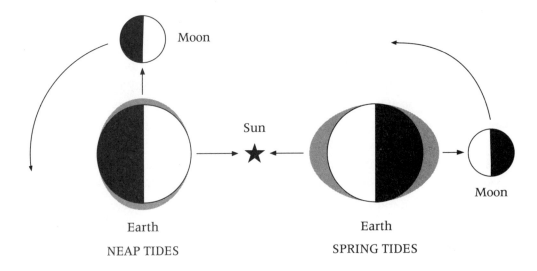

When the Sun, Earth, and Moon are in a straight line (top), the combined gravitational attraction of the Sun and Moon raise higher than normal tides on Earth, called spring tides. When the Sun and Moon are at right angles to each other with respect to Earth (bottom), the gravitational attraction of each is somewhat weakened and we have tides somewhat shallower than normal, called neap tides.

from under" the ocean water. This causes a second tidal bulge on the side of Earth opposite the Moon. This is why there are two big tides each day. If the Moon remained motionless over the Pacific Ocean, for instance, a great bulge of water would pile up there. But because the Moon moves around Earth, it pulls the bulge of water along with it. But because Earth rotates on its axis about 30 times faster than the Moon glides along in its orbit, Earth tends to drag the bulge along ahead of the Moon. When the bulge approaches the shore, there is a high tide; when the bulge is pulled away from the shore, there is a low tide. Because of its greater distance from us, the Sun's ability to raise tides is only one-third that of the Moon's.

Neap tides occur when the Sun and Moon are at right angles to one another. These are relatively weak tides because the Sun and Moon are attracting Earth's ocean water at right angles to each other. We have neap tides whenever the Moon is in first quarter or in last quarter. When the Sun, Moon, and Earth are lined up, at new moon and full moon, we have relatively high tides; they are called spring tides, but have nothing to do with the spring season. These tides are high because gravitational attraction of the Sun and Moon act together in a straight line rather than at right angles to each other.

EARTH'S CHANGING CLIMATE

Climate is defined as a region's weather averaged over a long period of time. Two major activities influence climate: (1) the amount of energy from the Sun that reaches Earth's surface; and (2) the amount of energy and matter, such as dust, carbon dioxide, and other chemical agents that are exchanged between the atmosphere and Earth's surface.

Climate is relatively warm at the equator and to 25° or so north and south latitude. The Sun's rays tend to strike that band of land and water more directly than at higher latitudes, which results in relatively more heat absorption by the ground and water. And because the solar radiation at high latitudes must penetrate a greater depth of atmosphere on its way to the ground, more of the Sun's energy is absorbed and reflected away by the atmosphere at higher latitudes.

Climate affects cultural development and many other human activities— the way we design our buildings, the way we dress, where we choose to live, how active we are at work and play, and so on. Throughout history climate change has caused many animal species to relocate to new environments or perish during the onset of drought or an ice age. Climate change that triggers an ice age causes significant changes in sea level—water is removed from the oceans and locked up as ice that covers many parts of high latitude regions for thousands of years at a time.

Climate has changed in cycles throughout Earth's four-billion-year history. For 90 percent of the last 550 million years Earth's polar regions have been free of ice, but ice is a common feature today, as it has been over the past million years. During that time, for example, at least seven ice ages have come and gone. The most recent one was at its peak only 18,000 years ago and retreated about 10,000 years ago. A relatively warm and stable climate in the Northern Hemisphere from about 1890 to 1940 was followed by a slight cooling. But such stable periods have existed during perhaps a mere 5 percent of the last 70,000 years. And usually they have ended quickly, most often lasting less than a hundred years.

Although some of the Sun's radiant energy that reaches Earth is reflected back to space (see diagram), some is retained. The amount retained is absorbed by carbon dioxide and water vapor in the air, and part is reradiated back toward Earth's surface again. This heat-trapping action of the air is called the greenhouse effect, and the gases that trap the heat are called greenhouse gases. Many climatologists claim that the release of huge quantities of greenhouse gases into the atmosphere through air pollution is increasing the greenhouse effect and triggering a period of warming.

Climatologists learn about Earth's past climates by examining fossils, lake and ocean sediments, peat bogs, glacial deposits, soils, and archaeological sites. Also, the widths of the annual growth rings of trees reveal temperature and rainfall changes over long periods. For instance, counts of tree growth rings date the period of drought that caused Colorado's Mesa Verde cliff-dwelling Indians to perish or flee during the years 1271 to 1285. Cause of the drought was a shift in the prevailing westerly winds. The once lush countryside of Greece apparently was dried up by a shift of the westerlies that brought drought and caused the death of the ancient Mycenaean civilization of 3,000 years ago.

Whereas the changing pattern of the prevailing westerlies influences climate change, the ocean currents play an important role in stabilizing climate. Water stores heat and carries it from one place to another as an ocean current flows from a warm region to a colder one. Half the heat moved northward and southward from the hot equatorial region is carried by ocean currents. The Gulf Stream, for example, begins as a narrow current of warm water flowing out of the Gulf of Mexico off the tip of Florida. It then flows northeastward and bathes and warms the shores of England, Scotland, Iceland, and Norway. Without the Gulf Stream the weather in those parts of Europe would be cooler. The harbors of Norway, for example, are kept ice-free all year by this warm Atlantic water from the Gulf of Mexico.

No single event can account for climate change. Ultimately the amount of solar energy reaching Earth is the major cause of climate. Solar energy input is determined by changes in the shape of Earth's orbit around the Sun, slight changes in the tilt of the planet's polar axis, and the time of year when Earth is nearest the Sun. Other influences include the amount of solar energy that penetrates Earth's atmosphere, natural and man-made changes in the atmosphere's content, changes in Earth's surfaces caused by continental drift, human interference with nature, and, possibly, variation in the Sun's energy output.

AN OCEAN OF AIR

We cannot describe the details of Earth's early atmosphere when the planet was formed. But it was unlike the air we breathe today, because it had very little oxygen. Oxygen was added to the air later, by the action of photosynthesis.

During the planet's molten stage many gases bubbled up out of the soupy rock and collected above the new planet as a primitive atmosphere. Among such gases there must have been large amounts of hydrogen, water vapor, nitrogen, carbon monoxide, and carbon dioxide. There may also have been smaller amounts of methane and ammonia. Solar energy would have split the water molecules into free oxygen and hydrogen. The lighter hydrogen would have escaped Earth's gravitational grip and been lost to space. The oxygen would have remained, and by combining with methane changed into carbon dioxide and more water vapor. Some such chemical evolution eventually led to the air we breathe today.

Held captive by Earth's gravity, Earth's ocean of air surrounds the planet to a depth of hundreds and thousands of kilometers. But 99 percent of the atmosphere is compressed into a layer about 30 kilometers (20 miles) deep. If Earth's atmosphere were removed, exposing Earth to the full force of the Sun's radiation, the planet would be as dead as the surface of the Moon or Mercury.

The air is a mixture of gases, dust from the land, salt from the oceans,

meteor dust, plant pollen, and volcanic ash. Most of the air—78 percent—
is nitrogen, which is important as a food for plants but is not used directly
by humans. Most of the remaining gas is oxygen; nearly all of Earth's
organisms depend on oxygen for life. About 1 percent of the air is a mixture
of water vapor, argon, helium, neon, ozone, carbon dioxide, and other
substances.

The atmosphere is structured in layers that blend into one another. The
light upper layers press down on the lower heavier layers and compress
them; at sea level, the air presses in on every square inch of your body
with a force of 14.7 pounds (in all, about a ton of air is pressing in on you).
At very high altitudes there is little air pressure; in fact, our body fluids
would boil out of us explosively if we were exposed to that condition,
which is why the cabins of high-flying aircraft must be pressurized. Although you would not die of explosive decompression if a jet airliner lost
its cabin pressure—because airliners do not fly high enough—you would
die of suffocation due to lack of enough oxygen.

THE TROPOSPHERE, the lowest and densest air layer, is where almost
all of our weather takes place. Over the United States the troposphere
reaches up to about 12,500 meters (about 40,000 feet), or nearly 13 kilometers (8 miles). On a hot August day the air temperature at the ground
may be 35°C (95°F), but at the top of the troposphere it will be −57°C
(−70°F). The temperature falls off at an average rate of 6°C for every 1,000
meters (or about 3.5°F per 1,000 feet). This temperature gradient, or slope,
occurs because radiant heat given off by the ground warms the air next to
the ground more than it warms the air higher up.

Air masses in the troposphere move over the land from regions of high
pressure to regions of low pressure as winds. As the Sun heats large, flat
areas of land, the air becomes lighter and rises, so vertical air currents also
occur. Although the lower troposphere contains large amounts of water
vapor, the top layer contains relatively little.

THE STRATOSPHERE rests on top of the troposphere and extends to an
altitude of about 50 kilometers (about 30 miles). The lower regions of the

stratosphere are swept by strong winds and are extremely cold. Higher up, however, the winds die and the temperature gradually rises (except over the polar regions in winter). At the top of the stratosphere the temperature is about −1°C (30°F). The cause of this warming is a layer of the gas ozone, which is a heavy form of oxygen consisting of three instead of two atoms. A blanket of ozone in the upper stratosphere blocks out most of the high-energy ultraviolet radiation from the Sun. Without the protective ozone layer, living organisms exposed to the full force of ultraviolet radiation would be seriously harmed or killed. Atmospheric pressure at the top of the stratosphere is only 1/1,000 the pressure at sea level, about the same as the atmospheric pressure in deep space.

THE MESOSPHERE sits atop the stratosphere as an air layer about 30 kilometers (20 miles) deep. It grows colder with height, falling to about −90°C (−130°F) near the top. At this altitude the air is so diffuse, or thin, that hardly any light is scattered about by the decreasing numbers of gas molecules. As a result, the sky appears to be nearly black, rather than blue. At lower altitudes the sky is blue because the blue wavelengths of sunlight passing through the air are bent and scattered more than the wavelengths of other colors. Scattering occurs because the air molecules are small compared with the wavelengths of blue light.

THE THERMOSPHERE is the top air layer and marks the borderline with space. At the top of the thermosphere, at an altitude of 30,000 kilometers (20,000 miles), the temperature rises to more than 1,093°C (2,000°F). But you must not compare this high "temperature" to the heat you feel on a hot summer day—there are too few gas molecules at thermosphere altitudes to transfer heat from the air to any object in the air. The same is true of sound. Neither heat nor sound can travel through the thinness of the thermosphere or the emptiness of space. The "temperature" of the thermosphere expresses the speed at which gas molecules are moving about. Any living creature exposed to the harsh conditions of the thermosphere would perish by being broiled to death on the side facing the Sun or frozen to death on the side in shadow—if it didn't explode first due to the near-zero pressure.

WHY THERE ARE SEASONS

Because Earth's axis is tilted with respect to the plane of its orbit by 23.5°, parts of the planet at certain times receive the Sun's rays more directly than other parts. When the north pole of the axis is tilted away from the Sun (see diagram), the Northern Hemisphere receives the Sun's rays at an angle, our period of winter. When the north pole is tilted toward the Sun, the Northern Hemisphere receives the Sun's rays in a direct line, our period of summer. Many people think that summer and winter are caused by the *distance* of Earth from the Sun. This is not so. Actually, during winter in

The tilt of Earth's axis of 23.5 degrees causes the seasons. When the Northern Hemisphere is tilted down and receives the direct rays of the Sun, we have summer. Six months later, the Northern Hemisphere is tilted up and receives the Sun's rays less directly, bringing on winter. It is not true that Earth is closer to the Sun during the summer months. It is closest to the Sun in January.

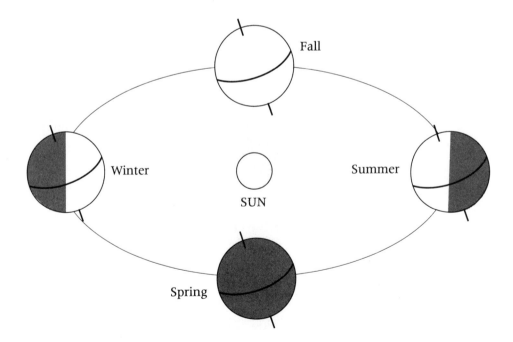

the Northern Hemisphere, Earth is closer to the Sun than it is during summer.

By keeping a record of the gradually shifting rising and setting points of the Sun on the horizon at different times of the year, you can understand why day length changes from one season to the next. The number of hours of daylight (in addition to the angle at which the Sun's rays penetrate the atmosphere) affects seasonal temperatures. On the first day of spring (about March 20) and the first day of autumn (about September 23), the Sun rises due east and sets due west. On those two days, called the equinoxes, the hours of darkness and daylight are about equal. Each day after autumn equinox, the Sun rises and sets a bit farther to the south on the horizon. In other words, the Sun traces an arc progressively lower across the sky day by day, which makes the days progressively shorter as we continue to move toward winter. About December 22, the Sun rises and sets at its farthest southward point on the horizon, giving us our shortest day of the year. That day marks the first day of winter and is called winter solstice.

After winter solstice the Sun's rising and setting points along the horizon begin to creep northward again. The days begin to lengthen as the Sun arcs progressively higher across the sky. By about March 20, the Sun once again rises due east and sets due west, reaching its spring equinox point. The days keep growing longer as the Sun arcs progressively higher across the sky. When the Sun reaches its northernmost rising and setting points on the horizon, we have the longest day of the year and the beginning of summer (about June 21), called summer solstice. The day after summer solstice the Sun's rising and setting points on the horizon begin to creep southward again; we head toward autumn and complete one year's cycle of seasons.

ENERGY SOURCES FOR EARTH

Civilization would be impossible without an adequate supply of energy. The cultures that have developed the highest standards of living, the most advanced cultures, are those that have most effectively harnessed energy to drive their technologies.

Today, three conditions, acting together, pose an urgent energy problem for the world's people: (1) a growing world population; (2) the efforts of Third World nations to become fully industrialized; and (3) the drive for unlimited growth and economic expansion of the rich industrialized nations. No matter how favorably or unfavorably we regard these conditions, each increasingly sharpens competition for the world's energy resources. To date, the fossil fuels of oil, coal, and natural gas have supplied the lion's share of energy to light homes, power factories, and serve as raw materials for the production of plastics, fertilizers, animal feedstocks, pharmaceuticals, and other products the world now depends on.

Some years ago we realized that Earth's supply of fossil fuels is limited and cannot sustain the world's present rate of development much longer. Although experts don't always agree on just how long "much longer" is, they do agree that shortages of fossil fuels will occur; it is just a matter of time. Demand and availability are the two key words when we consider nonrenewable energy resources: When demand exceeds availability, there is a problem. Consider, for example, petroleum, a nonrenewable fuel. Some experts believe that oil production will peak and then begin to decline around the year 2000, and that the planet's reserves of oil will be essentially gone in about a century. (Presently oil provides about half of the world's energy.)

Coal reserves are much more plentiful than oil reserves and are spread over larger regions. Given the global distribution of coal, it is very unlikely that any one nation or group of nations can control coal production in the way that the Arab states have controlled oil production. As a fuel resource, the relatively large deposits of coal can supply the world's energy needs for much longer than oil can, probably for several centuries. There is, however, a problem: coal is a "dirty fuel"; it is a major source of pollution, particularly by industry.

Nuclear *fission* energy is the most controversial of all energy sources. One danger is the possibility of a mishap that could release lethal amounts of radioactivity into the environment. In addition, the most effective nuclear power plants generate plutonium, which could be made available for use as nuclear bombs by terrorist groups. Of equal concern are the high-lev-elradioactive wastes generated by nuclear power plants and nuclear weap-ons factories.

Nuclear *fusion* energy is safer and cleaner than nuclear fission and is being investigated as an option. If the experiments are successful, the world's energy problems could be solved for hundreds or thousands of years. Fuel for nuclear fusion reactors is the hydrogen contained in the virtually limitless supply of ocean water.

GLOBAL ENERGY USE COMPARED WITH USE IN THE UNITED STATES		
ENERGY SOURCE	WORLD USE (Percent)	USE IN THE U.S. (Percent)
PETROLEUM	45.5	46.4
COAL	28.5	18.2
NATURAL GAS	18.3	28.2
HYDROELECTRIC	6.8	4.6
NUCLEAR	1.5	2.6

Oil, coal, and nuclear energy are the only energy sources that are suitable on a global level for certain needs, such as powering steel mills. But there are several other energy sources that could be used on local or regional levels: geothermal energy from underground heat, hydroelectric power from dams, ocean thermal energy, solar energy, tidal energy, wind power, and wood and peat. (Peat is partly decayed vegetable matter that accumulates in bogs over hundreds or thousands of years. Large deposits occur in Ireland, England, and the former Soviet Union.)

Wood and peat must be used less rapidly than their natural renewal rate, or they must be allowed to build up again. The same is true of geothermal energy. You cannot remove from the hot subsurface rocks of Iceland, Italy, or New Zealand, for example, more heat than the rocks can produce. If you temporarily drain them of their heat, you must leave them alone long enough to heat up again.

Solar collector panels work on a limited basis to tap energy in regions that have sunshine most of the time, but they are not practical on a large

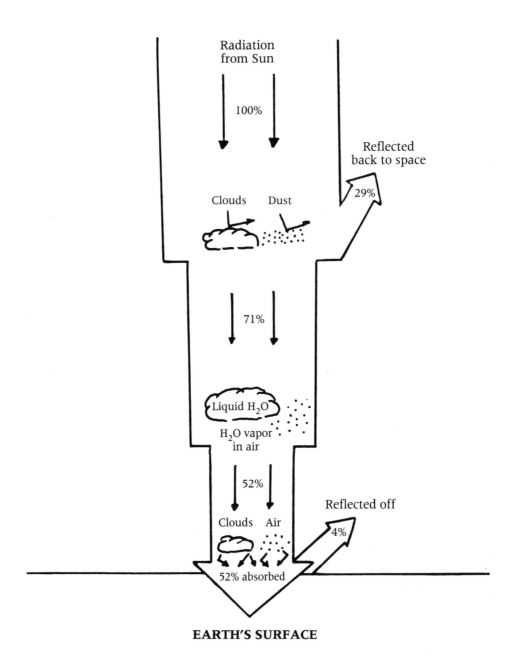

EARTH'S SURFACE

About two-thirds of the solar energy arriving at Earth is retained by the planet while an additional one-third is lost back to space.

scale in places like Maine or Washington state where clear skies are not the rule. Wind power, like solar power, is unpredictable but may be useful on a small scale—to provide supplemental energy for a house, for example. Tidal power, although predictable, is limited to coastal regions and could be used only for small-scale energy production.

The ultimate source of power, of course, is the Sun. In one second the Sun emits more energy than humans have used since we have been on the planet. Eventually, perhaps technologists will devise a way to collect solar energy from above the atmosphere, transmitting it as microwave energy to key collecting stations on the ground and then through a global grid to factories and homes. All other schemes to generate useful energy must be viewed as temporary efforts that tend to degrade the environment.

ATOMS AND MOLECULES

All matter is made of atoms, which are too tiny to be seen, even under the microscope. Without an understanding of what atoms are, and how they combine to form compounds, we cannot understand the nature of the force that holds a skyscraper together or keeps a biological system alive.

An atom is the smallest possible piece of those basic kinds of matter we call elements—gold, oxygen, iron, neon, uranium, and others. So the smallest possible piece of gold is a single atom of gold. Gold, or any other element, is a substance made up of the same kind of atoms.

No matter where an atom happens to be, its basic nature does not change. An atom of oxygen, for example, is the same whether combined with different kinds of atoms in a rock or inside a jellyfish. The oxygen (O_2) we breathe is a pair of oxygen atoms attached to each other. Such grouped atoms are called molecules. Atoms of different elements combine and form compounds. An oxygen atom joined to a carbon atom is a molecule of the compound carbon monoxide (CO), which is a toxic gas in automobile exhaust. Or two oxygen atoms may be joined to one carbon atom (CO_2) and called a molecule of carbon dioxide (the waste gas exhaled from our lungs). When two or more different kinds of atoms join—such as CO—a compound has been formed. Water (H_2O) is a compound of two hydrogen atoms bonded to one oxygen atom. Table salt (sodium chloride) is a compound of one atom of sodium joined to one atom of chlorine (NaCl). Some molecules, such as the important energy molecules of carbohydrates, proteins, and the DNA molecules of our bodies, are composed of dozens or hundreds or thousands of atoms.

Atoms are made of three basic building blocks called protons, neutrons, and electrons (see diagram). The simplest of all atoms is hydrogen. The center of the hydrogen atom, called the nucleus, is a single proton. A proton is a particle that has a positive electrical charge (written as $+1$). Moving about the proton nucleus is one electron. An electron is a much less massive particle and has a negative electrical charge of -1. The electron moves about the nucleus in all directions, forming a "cloud." Because the two opposite electrical charges cancel each other out, an intact hydrogen atom is electrically neutral. And because hydrogen has only one particle (its proton) in the nucleus, we write hydrogen as H, or H^1.

The second simplest atom is helium. Its nucleus contains two protons. But it also contains two neutrons. Unlike protons and electrons, neutrons are electrically neutral. Therefore, the nucleus of a helium atom has a positive electrical charge of $+2$ ($+2$ from the two protons and no electrical charge from the neutrons). Notice that helium has two electrons orbiting the nucleus. The combined electron charge of -2 balances the nucleus charge of -2, so an intact helium atom is electrically neutral. Because every

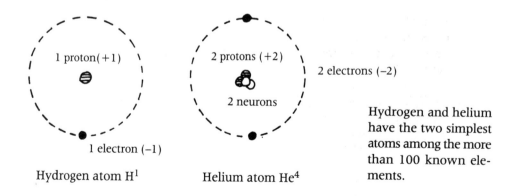

1 proton($+1$)

1 electron (-1)

Hydrogen atom H^1

2 protons ($+2$)

2 neurons

2 electrons (-2)

Helium atom He^4

Hydrogen and helium have the two simplest atoms among the more than 100 known elements.

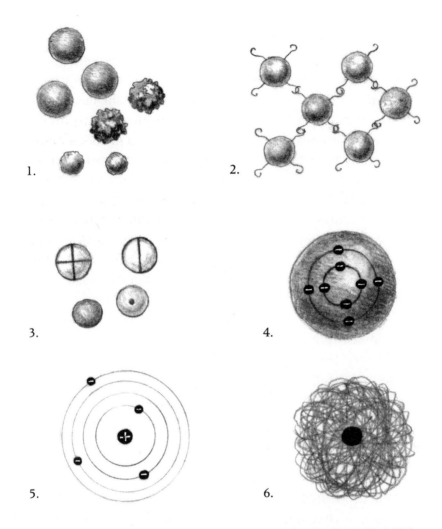

CHANGING CONCEPTS OF THE ATOM THROUGH THE AGES

1. Around 450 B.C., Democritus picured atoms as tiny lumps of matter that cannot be divided. Some were smooth, others rough, some large, some small. 2. Around 1630, Pierre Gassendi said that atoms must be hooked together in some way in order to form solids. 3. Around 1802, John Dalton said that atoms of different substances must differ in size and weight and that they combine as compounds. 4. Around 1897, J. J. Thompson pictured the atom as a positively charged globe with electrons inside. 5. Around 1913, Neils Bohr pictured the atom as having a positive nucleus surrounded by electrons orbiting in fixed shells. 6. Today we picture the atom as a cluster of positively charged protons and electrically neutral neutrons forming the massive nucleus, with electrons occupying certain fixed energy levels, the electrons being free to move from one energy level to another.

helium atom has four particles (two neutrons + two protons) forming its nucleus, it is written as He, or He^4. In all atoms, the number of electrons equals the number of protons in the nucleus. Further, the electrons are located at one or more allowed distances, called energy levels, from the nucleus.

The number of protons in an atom's nucleus determines its element's atomic number. Hydrogen, for example, has an atomic number of 1. Helium has an atomic number of 2, and so on through the remaining 103 elements listed in the standard table of chemical elements.

As the different kinds of atoms are arranged from number 1 (hydrogen) to 103 (lawrencium), they become increasingly heavier, because they have increasingly more protons and neutrons packed into the nucleus. An atom of gold, for instance, is heavier than an atom of helium, because each atom of gold has 79 protons and 118 neutrons in its nucleus, giving it an atomic weight of 197 (79 + 118). So an element's atomic weight is its total number of protons and neutrons.

Especially heavy atoms, such as uranium, have more than 200 protons and neutrons making up their nuclei. Lead is written as Pb^{206}. One form of uranium is written as U^{238}. Because uranium, and certain other elements, have so many neutrons and protons in the nucleus, they are unstable and tend to "decay" by losing nuclear particles. Such heavy unstable atoms are said to be radioactive.

HOW ATOMS COMBINE. Atoms join to each other by forming atomic "bonds." During a chemical reaction, atoms bond by sharing their outer electrons, or by transferring one or more outer electrons from one atom to another. Only electrons in the outer shell, or energy level, of an atom play a part in chemical bonding; the nucleus does not have a role in the process.

If an atom's outer shell has all the electrons it can hold, the atom will not bond with other atoms and is, therefore, said to be inert; neon, helium, and argon are examples. But atoms such as oxygen, sodium, chlorine, and hydrogen bond readily because their outer shells are not full. The electron sharing between two hydrogen atoms can be written H : H, each of the two dots representing each hydrogen's single electron. Electron sharing is the most common kind of chemical bonding.

The arrangement of an atom's electrons determines what chemical reactions can take place between it and other atoms, how much energy is needed to start the reaction, and how much energy is given off during the reaction. Three conditions influence the rate of chemical reactions: (1) the temperature, or kinetic energy of motion of the atoms; (2) the pressure, or force with which they collide; and (3) the number of atoms available to enter into the reaction. Chemical bonding is what holds most matter together and helps to keep you from falling apart.

RADIOACTIVITY

Reactions in the nuclei of atoms involve much more energy than the chemical bonding involving the electrons in an atom's outer energy level. In other words, *nuclear* reactions are much more powerful than *chemical* reactions.

The atoms of certain elements sometimes cast off one or more pieces of themselves as energy that we call radiation. In this process, called radioactive decay, the atoms of a radioactive element change into atoms of a different element. In the example shown in the box, uranium changes into thorium, and thorium changes into lead. There are other such transformation series. There is no way of telling which individual atoms in a sample will undergo decay, or when.

HOW URANIUM CHANGES INTO LEAD

KIND OF ATOM	ATOMIC WEIGHT	NUMBER OF NEUTRONS	NUMBER OF PROTONS	PARTICLE LOST
URANIUM	238	146	92	α
THORIUM	234	144	90	β
LEAD	206	124	82	STABLE

Most nitrogen atoms have seven protons and seven neutrons, so the atomic number of nitrogen is 7 (its number of protons) and its atomic weight

One of the many effects of radiation is demonstrated by this fern plant that took a picture of itself. When the fern frond's stem was placed in a solution containing radioactive sulfur–35, the frond took in some of the sulfur which then mixed with the frond's natural supply of nonradioactive sulfur. The frond was then placed against a photographic film. The radiation emitted by the S–35 traced an outline of the frond by "exposing" the film as it flowed through the frond. (*Brookhaven National Laboratory*)

is 14 (protons + neutrons). But one form of nitrogen has eight neutrons, so its atomic weight is 15 (N^{15}). Such "abnormal" versions of an element are called isotopes. Oxygen has eight isotopes. Some elements have as many as twenty.

Many isotopes are unstable. In an "attempt" to become stable, they throw off one or more of their neutrons, protons, or change neutrons to protons by emitting electrons. Such unstable isotopes are called radioisotopes. No one knows exactly why certain combinations of protons and neutrons produce a stable atom while other combinations do not.

TYPES OF RADIATION. The atoms of a radioactive element give off three types of radiation. An alpha particle is a cast-off cluster of two protons and two neutrons. Alpha particles are relatively heavy and slow moving and are stopped by the skin, but we can breathe them when they are in the air and we can swallow them when they are part of food. When an unstable isotope loses an alpha particle, the atom changes into another element that is four mass units lighter and two atomic number units lower, as in the case of uranium changing into thorium (see box on page 155).

Beta particles, the second type of radiation, are cast-off electrons. They are more energetic than alpha particles and can pass through flesh or several inches of wood, but they are stopped by a thin sheet of metal. An excess neutron in the nucleus of an unstable isotope may change into a proton. When it does the atom is given an extra + 1 electrical charge. In the process it casts away an electron (a − 1 electrical charge) as a beta particle.

Gamma rays, the third type of radiation, are waves of energy and are the most damaging. They can pass through several inches of steel or several feet of concrete. Gamma radiation, emitted as wave energy from the nucleus, is excess energy produced by the atom's loss of an alpha or beta particle.

Because each radioactive element has its own specific decay rate, radioisotopes can be used as "geological clocks."

HOW RADIATION HARMS US. Isotopes that give off all three types of radiation can be produced in three ways: (1) by the explosion of a nuclear test bomb; (2) by the millions of tons of waste material left over from the mining and processing of uranium for use in nuclear reactors and in bombs; and (3) by Earth's crustal rocks and the distant stars that hurl radiation onto us from space. The low-level natural radiation we are exposed to daily is called background radiation. Probably more than 90 percent of the man-made radiation we are exposed to zaps us when we visit our doctors and dentists for X-ray photographs. Radioisotopes and their lethal products, no matter what their source, become part of the air we breathe, the food we eat, and the water we drink and use to water our crops. They then get stored in our bones, in certain glands, and in other parts of our body where they do damage. And there is no way to get rid of them.

When a radioactive atom that we have breathed in from the air gives off a burst of damaging radiation, that radiation streaks through our soft body tissue, leaving a trail of damaged atoms in the cells it has passed through. It may disturb normal atoms by knocking off electrons, leaving the atoms with an electrical charge. Such atoms, called ions, may combine violently with other atoms or with molecules, killing or injuring the cell. After weeks, months, or years, cells injured in this way may begin to grow and reproduce in the wild manner that we call cancer. Radiation is a cause of cancer.

Cells damaged by radiation are affected in still other ways that we do not yet understand. If a damaged cell happens to be a human sperm cell or egg cell, which join and produce a new human being, the baby might be born deformed. Radiation also seems to make our bodies age faster, though the details of how this happens are not well understood. Despite our limited knowledge about the dangerous effects of radiation, we deliberately release more and more of it into the environment each year.

STATES OF MATTER

Virtually all matter can exist in different forms, or states. Temperature and pressure determine whether water, for example, is in a liquid state, a solid state (ice), or a gaseous state (vapor). Heating a lump of lead changes it from a solid state to a liquid state. As in any other solid, the lead atoms are locked into a more or less rigid arrangement, vibrating in place but not moving about very much. As we add heat the atoms begin to vibrate more vigorously. This energy of motion is called kinetic energy. As we add still more heat the atoms break their ranks and begin moving about past each other and bouncing off each other and the walls of their container. We have added enough kinetic energy to change lead from a solid state to a liquid state. The *melting* point of lead is 327°C (621°F).

If we add still more kinetic energy to the molten lead by increasing the temperature, it will boil away as a gas, or vapor. The lead atoms are no longer bonded to each other and fly about, freely bouncing off each other and the sides of their container as they collide. Their kinetic energy is high enough to overcome their tendency to form bonds. The *boiling* point of lead is 1,620°C (2,948°F).

If still more kinetic energy is added to a gas, the individual atoms collide so forcefully that their electrons are knocked out of their energy shells. This produces a gaseous soup of free electrons and free atomic nuclei that swim about independently. It is the condition in the gases of a star where temperatures reach from several thousand degrees in the outer regions of the star to millions of degrees in the star's core.

The cores of the Sun and other stars are crammed with hydrogen nuclei (single protons), which move about so fast and collide so forcefully that they fuse and build the nuclei of helium atoms. During the process, some of the matter is changed into energy, which is how stars shine and produce their enormous outputs of radiant energy. If only one gram of matter were completely transformed into energy, it would yield as much as the burning of 2,000 tons of gasoline, or would keep a 1,000-watt light bulb burning for 2,850 years. Temperature determines the amount of kinetic energy with which atoms collide and is, therefore, important in bringing about nuclear reactions inside stars and chemical reactions within our bodies and in the laboratory.

The chaotic state of atomic affairs in the core of a star is very different from the highly ordered arrangement of atoms in some crystals, such as quartz, diamond, and halite. Halite (common table salt) has its atoms of sodium and chlorine arranged in a fixed geometric pattern. If you look at several tiny halite salt grains through a magnifying glass you will see that each piece has the general shape of a cube. If you crush one of the tiny cubes it will break apart into many more pieces, and each of these pieces will also be a cube. If you could keep on breaking the cubes into smaller and smaller cubes, eventually you would end up with the smallest possible cube of halite—one with fourteen chlorine atoms bonded to thirteen sodium atoms. When enough of these tiny cubes are chemically bonded, you can see the cube shape. Such regular shapes made by atoms arranged in a fixed pattern, when visible to the naked eye, are called crystals.

MATTER AND ENERGY

Matter is anything that has mass and takes up space. You, for instance. Energy is the capacity to cause a change, or the ability to do work. Throughout the Universe energy flows along countless paths, transforming itself endlessly in many ways—from chemical energy into mechanical energy and from electrical energy into mechanical energy, for instance.

Energy occurs in two states—potential energy and kinetic energy. Potential energy has the ability to do work but is not doing work at the moment. Water held behind a dam is an example of potential energy; when the gates of the dam are opened, the force of gravity draws the water downhill and converts the water's potential energy into kinetic energy of motion.

The world around us (and each person's body) is kept active by four different forms of energy:

MECHANICAL ENERGY. When motion is transferred from one object to another, mechanical energy is involved. For example, when a golf club strikes a ball, the motion of the club head is transferred to the ball.

CHEMICAL ENERGY.   When atoms and molecules react with one another by breaking and forming chemical bonds, chemical energy is released. Breaking the bonds of certain energy-rich molecules in our bodies releases potential chemical energy as heat, or kinetic energy. That kinetic energy of motion is then used to drive other chemical reactions that require energy.

ELECTRICAL ENERGY.   A battery stores potential electrical energy that can be used to turn a car's starter, operate a computer, or turn on a light. Electrical energy sends signals along our nerve pathways when certain atoms associated with the nerves gain or lose electrons.

RADIANT ENERGY.   Light, heat, X rays, and radio waves are radiant energy. Radiant energy can be released from the energy of motion when electrons fall inward from a higher energy level (shell) to a lower one. The fall produces a particle, or quantum, of radiant energy called a photon. We see a photon as a miniburst of light. As the gas atoms in a flourescent neon light tube are excited by electricity flowing into the tube, electrons of the neon atoms change energy levels and give off billions of photons that flood the room with light.

Depending on the kinds of atoms involved and the size of the energy-level jumps, we see red photons, blue photons, orange photons, and so on. Very high-energy photons, such as gamma-ray photons, are produced in the nuclei of atoms deep within stars. The Sun and other stars produce their energy by converting hydrogen nuclei into radiant energy according to Einstein's equation $E = mc^2$. Quite simply, that equation says that energy (E) and mass (m) are interchangeable, a concept that has changed the way physicists, chemists, and philosophers have come to view the Universe.

Life on Earth is maintained by the ways radiant energy from the Sun is used and changed by living systems. When sunlight shines on a green leaf, the radiant energy causes molecules of water and carbon dioxide within the leaf to combine and produce sugar molecules (this is called "photo-synthesis"). The leaf has transformed the radiant energy of sunlight into chemical energy stored in the sugar. When we eat a leaf of spinach or lettuce, our body chemistry breaks down the sugar and uses its stored chemical potential energy to move our muscles. The chemical energy has been transformed into mechanical energy; along the way, some of the energy is lost as heat, never to be recovered.

THE LAWS OF THERMODYNAMICS

The laws of thermodynamics apply equally to an automobile in motion, to a star, and to a starfish. These laws cannot be broken, not even by the cleverest energy thief. Over the ages matter and energy ebb and flow among all living matter and between living matter and the physical environment. The total amount of matter and energy does not change. Only their form and location change. The amount of potential energy stored in a boulder sitting on the top of a hill is equal to the amount of mechanical energy it took to push the boulder up the hill. This concept is explained in two laws of thermodynamics:

First law: *Energy can neither be created nor destroyed, but can only be changed from one form to another.* In the energy system of a moving car, the energy of the gasoline is not destroyed. It is transferred through friction from the car to other systems, including the air and the highway. Eventually the entire mass of gasoline is transformed into heat. What happens during the transfer is explained by the second law of thermodynamics.

Second law: *When energy is transformed, some of it is changed into a type that cannot be transferred any further.* After each energy transformation, the amount of energy available to a system becomes a bit less than before because some is lost as heat. This occurs in a car as energy is used to overcome the friction of the pistons moving up and down in the cylinders. That is why we have to keep pumping more gasoline into the tank to keep a car going. This law might be stated as "There's no such thing as a free lunch." If the eater of the lunch doesn't pay, someone else does.

What do these laws mean to you as a living system, or to planet Earth as an environmental system, or to the Sun as a stellar energy production system? To you as a living system, the laws of thermodynamics mean that you need a continual input of food-energy for growth and maintenance. To prevent increasing entropy, or disorder, requires an input of energy that goes through continuous transformations, with unrecoverable heat loss all along the way. With an understanding of that principle, you should be able to explain why the notion of a perpetual motion machine is impossible.

To Earth as an environmental system, the laws mean that the planet needs a continuous input of solar radiation energy to maintain the growth of its green plants, which are the plant's primary food producers, and to power the millions of other planetary energy systems, including weather, atmospheric, and ocean circulation patterns. The source of 99.994 percent of the energy that flows through the global environment is the radiant energy from the Sun. The rest comes from tides, meteorites, natural radio-activity, moonlight, and starlight. Without energy from the Sun, all of Earth's energy systems would grind to a halt.

To the Sun as a star, the laws mean eventual death. The Sun has only a limited amount of hydrogen fuel in its core; in other words, it has a limited amount of usable mass that can be transformed into energy. When that usable mass is gone (when the gas tank runs dry), the Sun will stop shining. It will stop radiating the energy needed to drive all the living and nonliving energy systems of Earth. At that time, some five billion years from now, Earth and the rest of the Solar System will become a dead place for lack of energy.

Physicists use the word "entropy" to describe affairs governed by the second law of thermodynamics. Entropy is a measure of energy disorder in a system. All energy systems act to increase entropy, or to increase disorder. Consequently, any energy system tends to become increasingly disorganized as its available energy decreases. For example, hydrogen mass in the interior of all stars continues to be used to produce energy; eventually, all of the available mass-energy will be transformed and lost as heat. Unfortunately, lost heat cannot be recovered and converted back into useful energy. Physicists describe this situation as the "running-down of the Universe," or the "heat-death of the Universe."

GRAVITATION AND ELECTROMAGNETISM

The tides pulse, a sky diver falls to earth, rivers flow and the planets remain in more or less stable orbits about the Sun. All because of the force of gravitation. Gravitation also gives stars and planets their sphere shapes by tending to pull their matter toward the core, or center of mass. This "universal law of gravitation" applies to all things we can measure in the Universe, from the tiniest atom to the most distant galaxy.

Although no one knows what gravity *is*, the seventeenth-century physicist Sir Isaac Newton described how it works. Any two objects in the Universe, no matter what their mass, attract each other—two galaxies millions of light-years apart, two stars across the galaxy from each other, Earth and the Moon in orbit around each other. It is the force of gravity of Earth's center of mass tugging on us that prevents us from being flung off into space by the planet's spinning motion.

Two conditions determine the gravitational force with which two objects attract each other. One is mass, or the amount of matter packed into an object. The more massive two objects are, the greater the force of attraction between them. If the mass is doubled, so is the force of attraction. The other condition is distance. The greater the distance between two objects, the less the force of attraction. In this case, however, if the distance is doubled the force is not twice as weak but four times as weak. When the distance is tripled, the force is nine times as weak. In other words, distance affects the force of gravitation according to the inverse square law.

The Sun is more massive than the Moon, but the Moon is closer to us; consequently, the Moon has a greater effect on ocean tides. If the Moon's distance from Earth were halved, the force of gravitation would not be doubled; it would be four times greater. If the Moon were four times closer that it is now, gravitational attraction would be sixteen times greater. Again, the inverse square law.

The distances between the Sun and its widely scattered planets affect the planets' orbital velocities. A planet closer to the Sun needs a higher orbital velocity to counteract the Sun's gravitational attraction than does a planet farther away from the Sun, where the attraction is weaker. If Mars, for instance, moved in to occupy the much closer orbit of Mercury but kept its present, relatively slow orbital speed, Mars would be gravitationally drawn into the Sun and vaporized by the Sun's intense radiant energy. The following table compares the distances and orbital velocities of the nine planets.

DISTANCES AND ORBITAL VELOCITIES OF THE NINE PLANETS

PLANET	AVERAGE ORBITAL SPEED (kilometers per second)	MEAN DISTANCE FROM SUN (millions of kilometers)
MERCURY	48	57.9
VENUS	35	108.2
EARTH	30	149.6
MARS	24	227.9
JUPITER	13	778.3
SATURN	9.6	1,429
URANUS	6.8	2,875
NEPTUNE	5.4	4,504
PLUTO	4.7	5,900

Although two atoms are attracted to each other by the force of gravitation, there are much stronger forces that attract atoms and molecules. They are called electromagnetic forces and are trillions of trillions times stronger. It is the electromagnetic force acting between an atom's positively charged protons in the nucleus and its orbital electrons that hold the atom together, or that keep it bonded to other atoms in a compound. Electromagnetic forces also cause sparks, clothes to cling to our body, and lightning.

ELECTRICITY AND MAGNETISM

You can probably name at least a dozen things that need electricity to work. Electricity is such a common part of our lives today that we hardly give it a thought, unless the lights go out or we get a shock.

STATIC ELECTRICITY.   As early as 600 B.C., Greek scholars discovered that when a piece of fossilized tree resin (amber) was rubber with fur, the amber would "pick up" a feather or a piece of thread. The object would cling to the amber for a while and then fall away. The Greek word for amber was *elektron*. About 2,000 years passed before anyone figured out what gave the amber its power. Today we know that it was the manipulation of electrons, which we call electricity.

Vigorously rubbing a glass rod with a piece of silk is one way to manipulate electrons and produce electricity. The piece of silk scrapes electrons away from some of the atoms of the glass rod and transfers them to itself. Depending on how many electrons an atom has in its outer shell, the atom will either give up one or more electrons or accept additional electrons. When negatively charged electrons are removed from the glass rod, the rod is left with a positive electrical charge; the piece of silk has gained a surplus of electrons and has acquired a negative charge. How do we know? If you hold the glass rod and the piece of silk an inch or so apart, they will jump together. They will cling to each other until the piece of silk has given up its surplus electrons and the glass rod has reclaimed its lost electrons.

When you scrape your shoes along a carpet, you scrape electrons off the carpet and become negatively charged. If you then touch a metal doorknob, or your dog, a little spark will jump from your finger. You have created a mini-bolt of lightning. This movement of electrons is called static electricity. Real lightning is static electricity on a grand scale: Surplus electrons in a cloud are attracted to the positively charged ground in a sudden discharge that we see as a gigantic spark.

CURRENT ELECTRICITY.   Static electricity is chaotic. Current electricity is orderly, or "organized." Current electricity consists of electrons moving predictably along a pathway called a conductor. There are poor conductors, semiconductors, good conductors, and superconductors. Air is an example of a poor conductor; fresh water is better, salt water is better still, and metals such as copper and silver are best. Whenever electrons flow along from atom to atom through a wire, the flow is called a current.

A current also can involve the flow of positive charges, as it does in liquid conductors such as salt water. In a liquid there is a two-way movement of charges—positive charges move in one direction, and negative charges move in the opposite direction. Both kinds of charges are involved in the current of a liquid conductor. Therefore, we can define a current as the movement of an electric charge from one place to another; an electric charge in motion.

The force needed to push a current along a wire is measured in volts. A current has to be pushed along because the electric charges in motion cause electric friction. The higher the voltage, the greater the push. The amount of force pushing the flow of electrons through the wires of your house is about 120 volts. Whenever the lights flicker or dim briefly, the voltage may drop to 110 or so. The amount of resistance a conductor shows against the flow of electric charges through it is called just that—resistance. A steel wire has more resistance to current flow than does a wire made of copper or silver. A long wire puts up more resistance than a short wire. A thin wire has more resistance than a fat wire. Glass and rubber have so much resistance that a current will not flow through them. Such materials are called insulators. To protect people from electric shock, the copper wire of a lamp cord is wrapped with rubber insulation. And, the ceramic fixtures atop some telephone poles act as insulators.

Some electrically conducting materials have no resistance whatever and are, therefore, called superconductors. If current is fed into a ring made of a superconductor material, the current will keep flowing around the ring indefinitely and will not lose strength after the current source has been disconnected. Mercury, lead, aluminum, uranium, and several other metals become superconductors when their temperature is lowered to a few or several degrees above absolute zero. (On the Fahrenheit temperature scale, absolute zero is −460°.)

MAGNETISM. Magnetism is a close cousin of electricity. It apparently was detected around 550 B.C. by a Greek scholar who discovered that a piece of iron oxide, a natural magnet called a lodestone, would attract metal. Later it was found that a steel needle stroked by a lodestone was given the magnetic property of the lodestone itself. It was further discovered that such a magnetized needle would point along a north-south line when allowed

When tiny filed-off pieces of iron are sprinkled over and around a bar magnet, the filings fall along the magnet's lines of force. (*Photo by the author*)

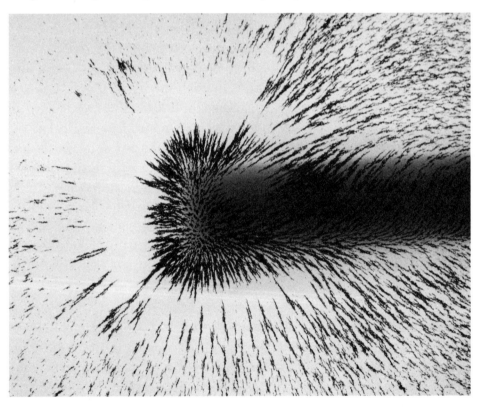

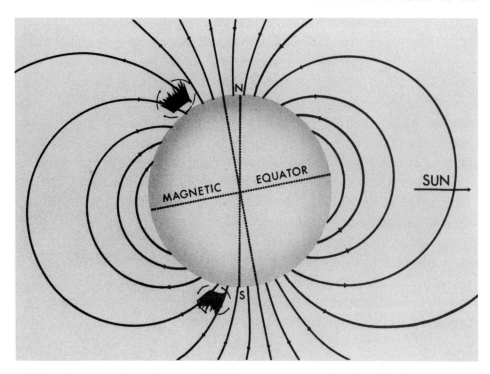

Earth, like many other planets, has a magnetic field with lines of force arranged as if a giant bar magnet were positioned inside the planet from north to south. Charged particles from the Sun sweep across space and are caught up in the north and south polar regions of Earth's magnetic field. At such times we may see dramatic displays of Northern Lights. (*NASA*)

to float freely. Then someone managed to balance a magnetized needle on the point of a small column, enclose it in a box, and call it a compass.

The property of magnetism takes us right back to electrons. Every electron is a tiny magnet that sets up a magnetic field, such as that surrounding a bar magnet. Each electron spins. If an atom has only one spinning electron, the atom has a weak magnetic field. If it has two electrons, both spinning and pointing in the same direction, it has a stronger magnetic field, and so on. However, if one of two electrons spins in the opposite direction, it cancels out the atom's magnetism.

In most substances each atom's electrons are spinning and pointing every which way so there is no alignment to produce a collective magnetism. But some substances, such as iron, nickel, and cobalt, have electron arrangements that favor magnetism. Iron is the most strongly magnetic because several of its electrons all spin and point in the same direction, making each of its atoms act as a single magnet. When you rub a steel needle with the end of a bar magnet, you align the needle's electrons so they all point in the same direction. But eventually the needle will lose its magnetic property as its vibrating atoms gradually disrupt the alignment of spinning electrons.

In the 1820s, the English scientist Michael Faraday discovered that there was a connection between magnetism and electricity. He demonstrated the connection by moving a magnetized bar in and out of a coil of wire (see diagram). Each time the bar was moved either in or out, an electrical current was set up in the coil as the magnet's lines of force cut across the wire. Faraday's work later led to the invention of electricity generation by dynamos and to the transformer.

In the 1820s the English scientist Michael Faraday discovered that when he moved a bar magnet in or out of a coil of wire, the cutting of the magnet's lines of force by the wire produced an electric current that could be measured by a galvanometer.

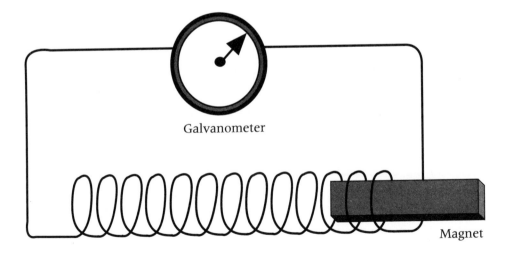

Galvanometer

Magnet

HOW THINGS MOVE

Everything is in motion. Atoms and molecules vibrate and dart about. Planets revolve around their local star, stars revolve around the center of their galaxies, and the vital parts of every living organism are in motion day and night. For the Universe there is no rest.

Motion is relative, because there is no fixed, motionless point in the Universe from which to judge motion. As you read this, you may be motionless relative to the room, but Earth's rotation is speeding you along at about 1,000 miles an hour relative to Earth's center. And as you walk along the aisle of a jet liner in flight you have one motion relative to the airplane and another, much faster motion relative to the ground.

During the 1700s the English scientist Isaac Newton worked out the universal law of gravitation. He found that falling objects at Earth's surface speed up, or accelerate, at the rate of 32 feet per second per second: after one second an object falls at 32 feet per second, after two seconds it falls 64 feet per second, after three seconds 96, after four 128, after five 160, and so on. Newton's work explained the force that keeps the planets in their orbits around the Sun. (The nature of that force had puzzled astronomers since ancient times.) Newton also discovered the following three laws describing the motion of objects.

First law: *A moving object will keep moving in the same direction and at the same speed until an outside force acts on the object.* And an object at rest will remain at rest until an outside force acts on it.

Second law: *When a force acts on an object, the speed or direction (or both) of the object's motion change.* The change is in the same direction as the force. The change is also proportional to the force but inversely proportional to the mass. In other words, it takes more force to push a piano than to push a shopping cart.

Third law: *For every action there is an equal and opposite reaction.* If you fire a shotgun you feel the gun "kick" against your shoulder. If you paddle a kayak the force of a paddle stroke toward the rear of the kayak (action) moves the kayak forward through the water (reaction).

THE ENERGY SPECTRUM

There is energy that warms you, that gives you sunburn, that astronomers collect in radio telescopes, that you see as a sunset, or that reveals the intimacy of your bones to an X-ray technician. All of that energy originates in the Sun and is spread out along a broad energy band called the electromagnetic spectrum.

All of that energy travels at the speed of light across the vacuum of space, and all of it travels as wave energy. Collectively it is called radiant energy. Einstein showed that this radiation carries its energy in bundles called photons. The amount of energy in one photon is inversely proportional to

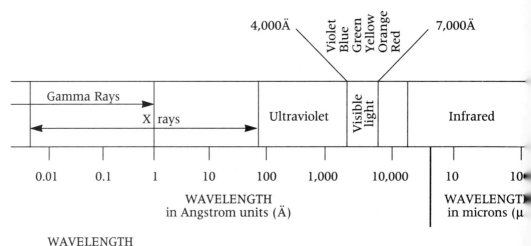

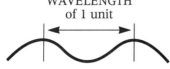

the wavelength of the radiation; that is, the shorter the wavelength, the more energy delivered per bundle.

At one end of the electromagnetic spectrum is the most lethal radiation known—gamma rays. Gamma rays have the shortest wavelength of all radiation, which means they are the most penetrating. Wavelength is measured as the distance from the top of one wave to the top of the next wave. The waves of ocean swells may have a wavelength of twenty feet or more, but the wavelength of high-energy radiation is measured in tiny fractions of a millimeter.

Next along the electromagnetic spectrum are X rays, somewhat less energetic than gamma radiation but still highly destructive. Next is ultraviolet (uv) radiation, which has somewhat longer wavelengths. Although less

Radiant energy from the stars and other objects in space ranges from the highly damaging gamma radiation at one end of the electromagnetic spectrum to radio waves at the opposite end. By studying these energy "windows" on space, scientists learn about the composition and structure of the universe. Radiant energy is measured in wavelength from the crest of one wave to the crest of the next wave.

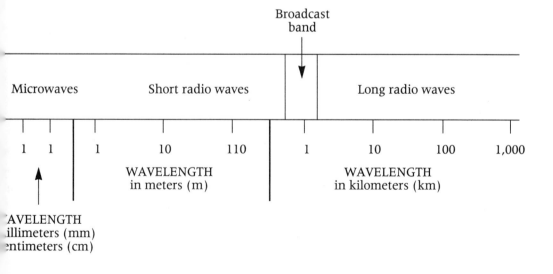

damaging, it can produce a painful sunburn in less than an hour. Visible light has wavelengths that our eyes are sensitive to, so we see this radiation. Beyond visible light, at still longer wavelengths, is heat radiation which we call infrared. Some 60 percent of the Sun's radiation is in the infrared portion of the spectrum.

Beyond infrared on the energy spectrum are the microwaves that cook your lunch, and at still longer wavelengths measured in centimeters, meters, and kilometers are radio waves, the least energetic of all electromagnetic radiation.

When a glass or plastic prism is held just right in sunlight, the white light is broken apart into its full rainbow range of colors that can be displayed on a paper screen. Violet light, with its relatively short wavelengths, is the most energetic; red, at the opposite end, has relatively long wavelengths and is the least energetic. The sensory cells in our eyes can detect that narrow range of wavelengths but not the wavelengths that are longer than red or shorter than violet.

When the Sun is on the horizon the colors we see may vary from one day to the next. At sunset (as at sunrise), the Sun is near the horizon and is shining through a greater thickness of air than when it is overhead. It also is shining through more of the dust and water vapor that always hang in the air. At such times, all the wavelengths of visible light shorter than orange and red are scattered about so much that their brightness is greatly weakened and we cannot see them. Instead, we see the longer orange-red wavelengths, which are scattered much less and so remain bright.

Although most animals depend largely on wavelengths within the visible spectrum to gain information about the world, some, such as honey bees, can "see" in parts of the ultraviolet band.

Modern technology enables astronomers to use energy all along the electromagnetic spectrum as windows on the Universe. There are gamma-ray observatories high in the sky that give us information about the centers of distant galaxies, and there are radio telescopes on the ground that tell us about the composition and structure of our home galaxy. As one astronomer has put it, "there's more to light than meets the eye."

MOTIONS OF THE EARTH, MOON, AND SUN

EARTH-SUN MOTIONS. Like the other planets, Earth is held gravitational captive by the Sun. At its particular distance from the Sun, Earth has a mean orbital velocity of 18.6 miles a second, which is about 67,109 miles an hour. Due to an increase in gravitational attraction when Earth is closest to the Sun (about January 3), its orbital velocity is speeded up a bit. When the planet's orbit takes it to its most distant point from the Sun (about July 4), Earth's orbital velocity slows a bit. The change in speed occurs because the orbit is an ellipse rather than a circle.

The planet's motion around the Sun is called its revolution. A year is the length of time it takes Earth to complete one revolution every 365¼ (mean solar) days. (A "mean solar day" is explained below.) Our calendar year is not that accurate and is rounded off to an even 365 days, ¼ day too short, which is why we add one day (February 29) every four years to keep the calendar in pace with the seasons. We call that special year Leap Year. The calendar year is measured by Earth's motion relative to the Sun's apparent motion against the background stars and is termed a tropical year, or year of the seasons.

If we measure one revolution around the Sun relative to the stars, rather than to the Sun's apparent motion, a year is about twenty minutes longer and is termed a sidereal (meaning "star") year.

In addition to Earth's revolution around the Sun once each year, Earth also rotates on its axis once a day. For ordinary timekeeping, a day has twenty-four hours; that is, it takes twenty-four hours for the Sun to cross the line marking its high noon position on one day and return to it the following day. That kind of day is called the apparent solar day. But the length of the apparent solar day changes throughout the year because of Earth's changing orbital speed. The variation in orbital speed makes the apparent solar day longer in winter than in summer.

To even things out and give each day of the year exactly the same length of time, astronomers have invented the "mean" Sun, which does not vary its speed across the sky. Looking at it another way, they have invented a "mean" Earth, which moves in its orbit at a constant speed. The day based on that average day length is called the mean solar day. Apparent solar time, then, is sometimes ahead of mean solar time and sometimes behind it. (A sundial measures apparent solar time and, therefore, doesn't agree with our watches very often.) The difference between apparent solar time and mean solar time is known as the equation of time.

As there is a sidereal year, there also is a sidereal day. It is the time required for a given star to cross the line marking midnight of one night and return to the same position the following night. Because the apparent position of the Sun is affected not only by the rotation of the Earth on its axis but also by its orbital motion around the Sun, a mean solar day is three minutes and fifty-six seconds longer than a sidereal day. Those extra four minutes for a mean solar day are accounted for in the following way: During the time it takes Earth to rotate once on its axis, the planet has moved forward a bit in its orbit. Consequently, the high noon position in the sky marked by an observer has also moved, and it takes the Sun an extra three minutes and fifty-six seconds to travel that extra distance across the sky. If Earth did not revolve around the Sun, the length of a solar day and a sidereal day would be the same.

EARTH-MOON MOTIONS. As Earth revolves about the Sun in an elliptical orbit, the Moon revolves about Earth in an elliptical orbit. The Moon's orbit varies the Moon's distance from Earth from 355,655 to 407,153 kilometers (221,000 to 253,000 miles), with an average distance of 384,462 kilometers (238,900 miles). A sidereal month is the time it takes the Moon to revolve about Earth once using the stars as markers. The sidereal month is 27 days, 7 hours, 43 minutes, and 11.6 seconds.

A synodic month—the length of time it takes the Moon to circle Earth once using the Sun as the reference point—is the length of time from one full moon to the next: 29 days, 12 hours, 44 minutes, and 2.8 seconds. A synodic month is longer than a sidereal month because Earth's orbital motion around the Sun and the Moon's orbital motion around Earth are in the same direction. The Moon's average orbital velocity around Earth is 3,679 kilometers (2,286 miles) an hour. At its distance from us, that means

From Earth we see the Moon go through phases, represented by the inner rim of moons in the diagram. But if you were in space above Earth's North Pole, the Moon would always appear to be half full (you would see only the outer rim), as would Earth. (*Courtesy of Cathie Polgreen*)

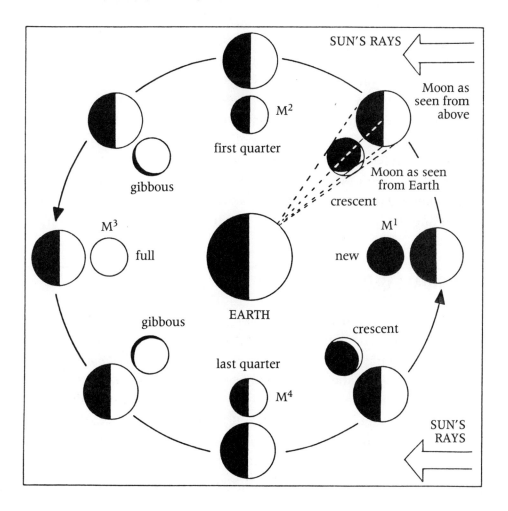

that every hour the Moon glides across the sky a distance a little greater than its apparent diameter, which amounts to about 33 minutes of arc per hour.

Although we always see the same side of the Moon facing us, the Moon does rotate on its aaxis. Then why don't we see the opposite side? It is because the Moon's rate of rotation is only one rotation for each revolution. Actually, we do see a little more than one-half of the Moon's surface—because of the Moon's orbital tilt of about 5° relative to Earth's orbital plane, and because of the Moon's irregularities in its orbital motion, it slowly teeters from side to side over the course of a month and shows us a bit more than half (59 percent) of its entire surface.

As the Moon travels in a complete circle around Earth each month, we see it go through phases. When the Sun, Moon, and Earth are in a straight line, with the Moon in the middle, we don't see the Moon at all because the side facing us is in shadow (position M^1 in diagram). At this point the Moon is said to be "new." As the Moon circles Earth we begin to see part of its surface reflecting sunlight. First we see it as a crescent and then as a half moon (position M^2). As the Moon keeps moving around and reaches the point opposite its new-moon position (position M^3), we see a full moon. We see another half moon when the Moon swings around to position M^4.

CALENDARS OLD AND NEW

Humans probably first "used" the sky as a means of keeping track of the passage of time. The apparent movement of the constellations across the sky by night could be used to accurately predict the time of sunrise, and the changing face of the Moon could be used to keep track of the passage of longer time intervals.

Imagine some ancient timekeeper—the first "astronomer"—cutting a notch in a tree or marking a stone each night as the Moon appeared. After a while people learned that between two full moons there were sometimes 29 days and other times 30 days, and that the year could be divided into

12 Moon months, or "moonths," totaling a year of 354 and a fraction days. For a few years this system of time reckoning is fine. But, as we know today, 11 days are lost each year (365 − 354 = 11). Over a period of six years, more than two months would be lost, and it would soon become apparent that the "moonth of bitter winds," or what we call January, would eventually be showing up in midsummer. The American Indians and other cultures also developed lunar calendars. The American Indians gave descriptive names to lunar months—"hunter's moon," "beaver moon," "snow moon," and so on.

By about 4200 B.C. the Egyptians probably had developed a solar calendar based on changes in the Sun's rising and setting positions along the horizon. They observed that about 365 days elapsed from the time the Sun rose in its farthest north position on the horizon (summer solstice, about June 21), and then, after moving to its farthest south rising position (winter solstice, about December 22), finally migrated back to its summer solstice rising position again.

The Mayan culture of Middle America also developed a calendar based on the Sun some 1,700 years ago. The Mayan calendar was remarkably accurate, giving the length of the year as 365.2420 days, compared with today's value of 365.2425 days!

The Roman emperor Julius Caesar decided that the old Roman Moon calendar, which had only 355 days to a year, plus an occasional leap month, should be changed to keep pace with the Sun year of 365¼ mean solar days. In revising the calendar in 47 B.C., he first adopted the solar year of exactly 365 days, but then found that he had a quarter of a day (or six hours) left over at the end of each year. To solve this problem, he decreed that every four years there would be an extra day added to the calendar (Leap Year). Today we refer to Caesar's calendar as the Julian calendar.

Still, the calendar did not keep pace accurately enough with the seasons over long periods of time, not even with a Leap Year. To further refine it, Pope Gregory XIII revised the calendar again in 1582. At that time the old Julian calendar was out of pace with the seasons by ten days and was lagging behind the seasons by 11¼ minutes a year. Over 1,000 years this difference added up to an error of 8 days. To correct this defect, the Pope brought the then existing calendar up to date by canceling 10 days: Thursday, October 4, was followed by Friday, October 15. When the change was announced to the public, angry mobs rioted, feeling that the Pope had robbed them of time and shortened their lives. There was much shouting, "Give us back our lost days!"

To keep the calendar in pace with the seasons in the future, the Pope's advisers proposed that three Leap Years be omitted every 400 years. From that time on, Leap Years have occurred every four years *except* when the number of the year ends in 00 and is not divisible by 400. For example, 1900 and 2100 are not Leap Years, but 2000 and 2400 are. This calendar is called the Gregorian calendar and is the one we use today. It seems to be accurate enough, because it gets out of step with the seasons by only one day in every 3,000 years.

KEEPING TIME

Time has a thousand definitions. There is no such thing as a "sense" of time, although we commonly use that expression. Time is subjective, each of us having our inner, private second hands that tick off the minutes and hours at rates that reflect our anxieties of the moment, or our peace of mind. The human body lacks the necessary biological rhythms to serve as an accurate clock. Although your pulse rate might be used to count off a minute of time (about 72 beats), another person's heart rate might be a bit faster or slower.

Using Earth's rate of rotation on its axis to measure a day and its revolution around the Sun to measure a year also fails to provide the timekeeping precision needed by modern civilization—aircraft navigation systems and computers demand time measurements in microseconds, not seconds.

To measure time, we need some device, natural or man-made, that behaves exactly the same way over and over again: repetitions that occur at a steady rate, with precision, and in units that can be counted and subdivided.

In the slower world of centuries ago, the repetitious and more or less regular motions of Sun and Earth served well enough. But because the modern world demands a greater precision, we have traded in the cuckoo clock for atomic clocks.

In 1967 atoms of the chemical element cesium[133] gave us a new definition of the time unit we call a second. Before 1956, one second was defined as the fraction 1/86,400 of the mean solar day. Today we speak of the atomic second. In modern technological parlance the atomic second is defined as "the duration of 9,192,631,770 periods of the radiation corresponding to the transition between the two hyperfine levels of the ground state of the cesium[133] atom." In simpler but less precise language, an atomic second is the number of vibrations of a cesium atom's electrons per second, making cesium one of the world's best atomic clocks. It keeps International Atomic Time with an accuracy of 1 second in 6,000 years, and within billionths of a second over short intervals of a minute or less. But there are different atomic clocks that don't lose or gain a second in 30,000 years! Other atoms that make especially good atomic clocks include rubidium, and hydrogen, and the ammonia molecule. The public receives its time tick indicating the exact pulse of noon as an average of various atomic time scales known as Universal Coordinated Time (UTC).

SPACE-TIME

Science forever stretches our minds by introducing new ideas that show us the world as it isn't, at least as it isn't in our day-to-day lives. One such idea, one that involves time, is the notion of space-time. The world of space-time is a strange place, but it is every bit as real as our here-and-now world. To understand what happens in space-time we must leave behind our world of everyday experience. Time is no longer absolute; it depends on the relative motions of the observers who keep track of the passage of time. The world of space-time is a fascinating place. What makes it so are the many strange ways in which the speed of light affects our lives there.

Before entering that world, consider how the speed of light affects our perception of an event right here in our Solar System home. Light, like a speeding automobile, requires time to move from one place to another. But light, remember, travels not at 65 miles an hour, but at 299,460 kilometers (186,000 miles) a *second*, which amounts to about 2 billion kilometers (670 million miles) an hour.

Suppose that one observer on Earth and another on Mars are studying activity in the Sun's surface gases. Suddenly a solar flare bursts into view. Light from the flare will cross the 150 million kilometers (93 million miles) to earth in 8.3 minutes. But 12.7 minutes elapse before the light reaches Mars, because Mars is 227,899,410 kilometers (141,614,000 miles) from the Sun. So the two observers do not see the same event at the same time. When the Voyager I spacecraft flew past Saturn in mid-November 1980, it was 1,281,000 kilometers (796 million miles) from home. The radio control signals sent from the Jet Propulsion Laboratory in California took 1 hour and 25 minutes to cross that 796-million-mile distance to reach Voyager I's antenna.

According to the laws of physics, no material object can either attain or exceed the speed of light. Although we could reach a speed of 99.9, or 99.99, or 99.99999 percent the speed of light, we could never quite reach 100 percent.

Nevertheless, something interesting happens at those near light speeds (called relativistic velocities), and here is where we enter the strange world of space-time. It is called time *dilation* and is part of Einstein's special relativity theory. It is a slowing down of time and has been demonstrated to be quite real. Put simply, time slows down for anyone traveling at relativistic velocities. For instance, a starship crew traveling at 99 percent the speed of light and making a round trip to the star Procyon—about ten light-years away—would return to Earth to find that friends and families were about twenty years older (10 Earth-years travel time to the star + ten Earth-years to return). But due to time dilation, the crew members' clocks would have kept slower time; crew members would have aged only three years according to their spaceship clock time and their body time.

Time actually would slow down for such a starship crew. Clocks and watches would run more slowly as the starship moved faster. Also, the starship crew's heartbeats, breathing, and all other body functions would slow down, as would their aging process. To the crew members, nothing unusual would seem to be happening. Whenever they varied the speed of their ship, they would alter the pace of time. They could slow time almost to a standstill (at 99.9999 percent the speed of light), but they could never stop it completely because they could never quite attain that last tiny fraction of the speed of light.

One graphic example of time dilation is called the twin paradox problem. At birth two twins named Randii and Robbii are sent into space for round-trip journeys to the twin stars Castor and Pollux in the constellation Gemini the Twins. Their cousin Sue, also the same age and hardly able to hold her head up, nevertheless waves them off. Randii travels at three-fifths the speed of light to Pollux, which is about 35 light-years away. Robbii travels at four-fifths the speed of light to Castor, which is a little more than 45 light-years away.

As the years pass, Sue, now able to hold her head up, plans the twins' homecoming. According to her timekeeping, Randii's total trip time will be 116 Earth-years. Robbii has to go a bit farther, but he is traveling faster, and his total trip time will be 112 Earth-years. Sue decides to plan two separate parties four years apart.

Because the clocks in the twins' spaceships tick off slower time than Earth-time, and because the twins age more slowly, Sue is in for a surprise when they return. First she greets Robbii who left 112 years ago her time. But because of Robbii's time dilation, Sue finds that he is only 67 years old, compared with her age of 112.

Four years later, Sue and Robbii go to the space port to meet Randii. His ship, recall, traveled slower than Robbii's, so Randii aged more rapidly than his brother. Sue is now 116 years old, and Robbii is 71. On joyfully meeting them, Randii announces that according to his clock time he is 92.

Although the three of them were the same age at the beginning of the trip, time dilation caused them to be different ages by the end of the trip. Thereafter, all three would age at the same rate in accordance with the same Earth-clock.

In space-time, does time *actually* slow down for those who speed among the stars? According to current knowledge, it does. Atomic clocks placed in fast-moving conventional aircraft have been measured; they tick off time more slowly than identical atomic clocks at rest on the ground.

Seven

SCIENCE AND HUMAN VALUES

MANAGING OURSELVES

WHAT ARE VALUES?

What are values? Are they unspoken rules of behavior handed down from one generation to the next over the ages? According to the writer James A. Michener, "Values summarize the accumulated folk wisdom by which a society organizes and disciplines itself." Values also are embodied in the teachings of various religious groups, and less-structured behavioral guides that we learn from our peers from the time we are very young. Values have roots in many sources—family, religion, peers, books, television, and motion pictures, all continuously interacting, sometimes in harmony and other times in conflict.

Consider the results of a 1989 survey of 1,093 high-school seniors polled by the Pinnacle Group, Inc., an international public relations corporation:

36 percent said they would plagiarize in order to pass a certification test.
67 percent said they would inflate their business expense reports.
50 percent said they would exaggerate an insurance damage report.
66 percent said they would lie to achieve a business objective.

Test your values—would you plagiarize, inflate, exaggerate, or lie to achieve an objective? Have you ever done so?

When questioned, most of us would say that personal values guide our decisions. But until we actually face an important decision, or have to demonstrate courage, honesty, or loyalty, for instance, we can't be *sure* how we will behave. When in doubt, we sometimes turn to others—our peer group, a teacher, a parent—for help in making a value-based decision.

187

At such times we may thoughtlessly accept a ready-made value held by a group or an individual we respect. Sometimes we discover that our values conflict with the values held by someone we admire and respect. In those situations, it is difficult, sometimes impossible, to choose a course of action. Values are intensely personal matters, and the degree to which we live and act in accordance with them determines our "character." Sometimes we find it hard to express a value in words. We simply feel or sense that a certain action is "right" and that a contrary action is "wrong." How can we account for these "unspoken" values?

MEDICAL INTERVENTION

More and more often modern science and technology present situations that no one has ever before faced. Modern medicine's new drugs and machines can prolong life beyond the state when an ill or injured person would live naturally, or beyond the stage when such a person might want to live. Should our laws allow us to end a person's life when requested to do so by the ill person (or on the request of the person's closest relative/friend when the person is unconscious)?

Nancy Cruzan, a 32-year-old woman, was unconscious for seven years due to injuries suffered in a car accident. Doctors agreed that she would probably never wake up. Despite this medical consensus, the courts ruled that Nancy's parents not be permitted to remove the feeding tubes that kept her alive as a "vegetable." The Missouri court, backed by the Supreme Court, concluded that people in general want to be kept alive as long as possible as "vegetables" rather than die with dignity and spare family and friends continued grief. Should a court have the collective moral right to impose such a value on individuals?

The law in New York state, as well as in Missouri, says that ill persons unable to refuse artificial life-sustaining treatment will automatically receive it; in other words, they will not be allowed to die. According to Marcia Angell, a physician and the executive editor of *The New England Journal of Medicine*, "What we need are legislative remedies . . . that will restore the rights of families and doctors to act in our best interests when we no longer can." The problem, of course, is who determines the meaning of "best interests"?

The following case may seem to be unrelated to Nancy Cruzan's situation. But it isn't, because it is another example of a personal value being raised to the level of a societal value, and it is at that level that the courts decide our lives.

David and Ginger Twitchell, a young married couple in Boston, Massachusetts, had a son Robyn who became seriously ill when he was two and a half years old. Robyn developed a severe bowel obstruction. In ordinary circumstances, the parents of such a sick child would take the child to a doctor. But the Twitchells chose a different form of "treatment"— prayer. They are Christian Science followers who do not believe in medicine. So they prayed for their son's cure. And they summoned the help of a "faith-healer" of the Christian Science Church. And they prayed together. Robyn, who had no say in the matter, did not get better. The child died five days later. What values were operating here? And whom, if anyone, did they benefit?

THE ABORTION CONTROVERSY

Abortion can be natural, or "spontaneous." Or it can be artificial, or "induced." In either case, it results in the death of the embryo or fetus and has been one of the most common means of birth control throughout history.

SPONTANEOUS ABORTION, also called miscarriage, takes place when the embryo does not develop or when the embyro or fetus dies of natural causes determined by the mother's health or behavior. Possibly as many as three-fourths of all pregnancies—confirmed and unconfirmed—end in spontaneous abortion. The number of spontaneous abortions in confirmed pregnancies is about 20 percent. A woman undergoing spontaneous abortion early in her pregnancy experiences cramps and blood loss typical of a normal menstrual period. Spontaneous abortions occurring later in a pregnancy produce more severe reactions, sometimes resembling the pains of childbirth.

INDUCED ABORTION. Most professionally induced abortions in the United States are performed within the first twelve weeks of pregnancy and are carried out by a method called vacuum aspiration. A suction tube inserted into the uterus removes the embryo and placenta. Abortions performed during the second twelve weeks are more complicated because of the embryo's continued development. After the sixteenth week the process may involve injection of either a salt solution or the hormone prostaglandin into the fluid sack enclosing the embryo. Although the second most common method, abortion by injection is somewhat less safe than the vacuum method. Abortion by either method during the first twelve weeks of pregnancy is relatively easy and virtually risk-free.

During the 1980s an estimated forty to sixty million induced abortions were performed worldwide, of which some thirty-three million were legal. In 1973 the United States Supreme Court eased laws restricting abortion, judging the old laws unconstitutional because they violated a woman's right to privacy. Since then the court has said that: the decision to have an abortion during the first twelve weeks should be left to the pregnant woman and her physician; individual states can regulate abortions during the second twelve weeks; and the states can prohibit induced abortion after the second twelve-week period.

The legalization of abortion dramatically reduced deaths and hospitalizations of pregnant women and promoted convenient and low-cost abortion clinics. During the 1980s more than half of all abortions in the United States were performed safely and legally in clinics.

In the United States the controversy over abortion has produced objections ranging from controlled protest to violent destruction of abortion clinics by fire and bombs. Many of those who oppose abortion do so on the grounds that a human being is being "murdered." The issue is seen largely from an emotional perspective. It also hinges on when an embryo or fetus should be regarded as a "human being."

The "right-to-lifers" claim that life begins at the moment of conception, or the instant a sperm cell and egg cell fuse. They further claim that every fertilized egg has a "right" to be born. And they contend that legalized abortion encourages teenagers to engage in sex and to feel that there is nothing socially undesirable or "wrong" about being an unwed mother, or an unwed father who abandons his female partner and baby.

People in the "pro-choice" camp argue that a fertilized egg (zygote) is not yet a human being, although it does have the potential to become one. They say that a "person" does not develop until the fetus develops a heartbeat and begins to kick and express a personality, or until the fetus is able to sustain its life without direct assistance from the mother. The pro-choice group also argues that legal abortion is safer than illegal abortion, and that a woman who gets a legal abortion is psychologically better off than one who has undergone an illegal abortion.

The inconsistencies in logic, appeals based largely on emotion, and contradictory stances so often exhibited by those who claim a right-to-life morality sometimes are difficult to understand. In an attempt to save a teenager's embryo, right-to-life groups use false advertising to trick a frightened and confused pregnant teenager into one of their so-called "abortion clinics," which are not abortion clinics at all. The teenager is then virtually forced to remain and watch videotapes showing mangled fetuses and screaming women undergoing induced abortion. Militant right-to-lifers also risk killing the people who staff legalized abortion clinics when they set fires or plant bombs. Although all right-to-lifers claim to have moral values regarding the sacredness of human life, for some those moral values seem to depend on whose life they happen to consider sacred at the moment.

GENETIC ENGINEERING

The 1970s ushered in a bold new era in the history of genetics. Biologists had learned to transfer the units of inheritance, genes, from one organism to another. The transferred genes become a permanent part of the recipient organism's hereditary system. This new biotechnology is called genetic engineering.

Geneticists now have the ability to transfer genes from one organism to another that lacks and needs them. They also have the possibility of substituting a healthy DNA sequence for a defective one in a human egg or sperm, thereby producing a healthy infant rather than one with a major genetic disorder. As a result we find ourselves living in a moment of history when a major biological discovery has generated moral, ethical, legal, social, and political issues never before faced.

Genetic engineering is closely related to another area of genetic research that also poses far-reaching ethical concerns. It is known as the Human Genome Initiative and involves identifying and mapping every human gene. "Never will a more important set of instruction books be made available to human beings," says the project's major supporter, biologist James Watson, who won the Nobel Prize for his discovery, with Francis Crick, of the structure of DNA. The project is expected to revolutionize medicine in the twenty-first century. It promises monumental progress in the diagnosis and treatment of disease. Genetic profiles of newborn babies will reveal genetic weaknesses to disease and spell out the steps needed to ease illness in later life.

But what of the possibilities of "misusing" such genetic profiles? Will big companies or the government require genetic screening before hiring? Will genetic profiles become as easily available to insurance companies and law enforcement agencies, for example, as computerized mailing lists are now? How will physicians advise families with a fatal genetic illness, such as Huntington's disease, for which there is no known cure?

Some biologists are openly hostile to the human genome project. Among them is biologist Salvador Luria, who has said that the project may be leading us into a "kinder, gentler program to 'perfect' human individuals by 'correcting' their [genetic makeup]."

One current face of the controversy over genetic research is the emotional notion of "tinkering with human life." If we have the ability through genetic engineering to cure a crippling genetic disorder in a person, or a potential disorder carried by one member of a couple wanting children, should we use that ability or not? And should the decision be made by society through legislation, or by the individual free of social restraints? Some argue that we are morally and ethically obliged to put such biotechnology to use where it is needed and wanted. Others argue that tinkering with human life, no matter what the motive, is morally "wrong." But what about parents who deliberately conceive a child while knowing that the odds of their child having a crippling genetic disorder are high?

Another face of the controversy is the following question: If research scientists agree to prohibit further research in genetic engineering, would that not be in contradiction to the principles of science—to investigate dispassionately and objectively every aspect of nature that can be investigated? Who is to say whether this or that aspect of nature is off-limits to scientific research?

Genetic engineering gives us the power to change the human population's gene pool by removing unwanted genes and adding wanted ones. But some people are opposed to such "tampering" with life. When left to its own devices, natural selection weeds out many genetically damaged individuals from the population and so prevents their defective gene(s) from entering the gene pool. That is how nature works without human interference. But by keeping such people alive with medical technology, we are keeping their unhealthy, and unwanted, genes in the population's gene pool. The result is that the unhealthy genes are passed on to those yet to be born. Is not that action also "tampering" with life?

We come to the aid of such genetically diseased people for "humanitarian" reasons, we tell ourselves, through consideration for the individual. Or is it really through consideration for ourselves? What about the consideration of society? Can we overlook that concern? Nature does not perform humanitarian acts.

Perhaps the largest question of all looming over the prospects of genetic engineering is whether we human beings yet have the collective social conscience required to take responsibility for ourselves as a species by directing our evolution through gene manipulation. No other species on Earth has had the capacity to alter its individuals by conscious design.

We are at a frontier of medical technology; it demands of us a degree of scientific literacy in biology to enable us to formulate and then exercise value judgments that involve our genetic future.

WORLD POPULATION GROWTH

The world's human population is growing at a rate that seriously concerns many scientists, politicians, and others. At the time the Paleo-Indians crossed over into the Americas from Asia some 30,000 or more years ago,

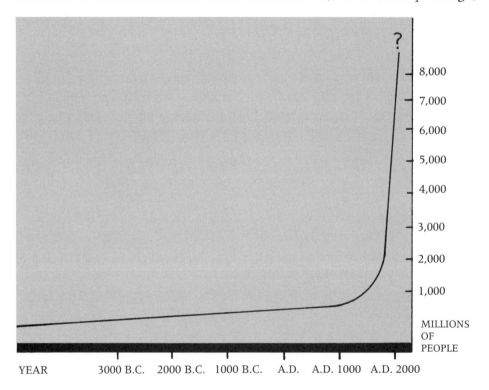

The human population growth curve is on a steep rise that alarms many people. No known population of organisms has ever grown at such a rate without experiencing a major change. Compare the rate of human population growth from 3000 B.C. to A.D. 1500 with the growth rate from the years 1500 to 2000. How much longer can the planet-wide ecosystem continue to support our uncontrolled production of ever more people? The answer is unknown.

the total world population probably was less than five million, the present population of Philadelphia. The world population today stands at 5.4 billion; it is expected to pass eight billion by the year 2020.

In many countries modern medicine and standards of hygiene have lowered the death rate, but birthrates continue to climb. In the United States our rate of new births plus the inflow of legal and illegal immigrants is resulting in continuing population growth. Each year we add the population equivalent of four cities the size of Washington, D.C.

The more people there are, the faster the world population grows. Around the year 1850 it took 150 years for the world population to double. Today the doubling time is about forty years, and in about three decades it may be only fifteen years. Just in the past century the world population has doubled three times. The world population is growing out of control. More and more people mean increases in the production of food, houses, and energy; billions of tons of manufactured goods; and much more pollution. What will happen to the quality of life as our numbers continue to increase?

Such questions must concern us, even if we do not yet have the answers. On Chesapeake Bay overdevelopment has contaminated the water quality and degraded shoreline ecology. In the Florida Everglades human competition for water and habitat has evicted or destroyed the local populations of many wildlife species, including the endangered Florida panther and peregrine falcon. On a worldwide basis, if population demands on the environment continue—and they are sure to—increased cutting of the planet's tropical forests could cause 25 percent of all wildlife species to disappear within the next fifty years.

When examining population growth, we must consider two things: (1) the number of people in relation to the available resources that the environment can supply; and (2) the impact on the environment imposed by the disposal of wastes. Both affect the quality of life.

Every year, as the world population increases, the risks of widespread and frequent famines, disease, and long-lived ecological disaster also increase. We can only hope that a rational population policy will become a worldwide reality before any such event spells doom on a global scale. But we have no assurance that it will, because we do not know whether the problem of a runaway world population *can* be solved rationally.

A more likely chain of events will be increasing numbers of famines that kill increasing numbers of people in Third World countries, where even now ten to twenty million people die of starvation each year. And as in the past, the response of the rich industrialized nations will be to send temporary food relief that will serve only to keep alive many of those who already live in misery, and they, in turn will produce still more offspring.

Even the rich industrial nations are feeling the pinch of too many people; however, it is happening gradually, and most of us do not realize that the quality of our lives is eroding from one year to the next, from one generation to the next. As Cornell University ecologist Peter Brussard has pointed out, "All of society's present ills—pollution, poverty, racism, social injustice, and war—are further aggravated by an expanding population. All must realize that as the population continues to grow, the standard of living will inevitably go down for all of us. Goods will become increasingly scarce and costs will rise. Pollution will increase, government interference and regimentation in our daily lives will increase, and individual privacy and freedom will decrease. Do we want to support many people marginally, or few people comfortably?"

MANAGING THE PLANET

Driven by the energy of sunlight, nature purifies the substances necessary for life by recycling water, carbon, oxygen, nitrogen, phosphorus, and other matter. The production of fresh water, for instance, needs only sunshine to first evaporate ocean water and then condense it out as freshwater rain. But when that rain becomes contaminated in the air by toxic emissions from industrial plants, it is turned into a destructive substance called acid rain.

When natural cycles, called biogeochemical cycles, are disrupted, the ecosystem's ability to support life lessens. An input of new energy is then needed to correct the problem. The problem, in one word, is *pollution*. Nature is unable to recycle our wastes as fast as we produce them. Acid rain and smog are damaging forests and people. Excess carbon dioxide and other greenhouse gases that our automobiles and factories release into the air are heating up the planet. Excess sewage and industrial chemicals are polluting our rivers and coastal waters. Toxic chemical dump sites across the country threaten underground water supplies. Excessive use of fertilizers in many areas is degrading the natural qualities of the soil. Each year, as world population continues to climb, we produce more and more pollutants that damage the environment, and us, because we are part of the environment, not apart from it.

THE VANISHING OZONE LAYER

Every time an old refrigerator or air conditioner is crushed for junk, a substance known as Freon is released into the air. Freon contains the gas chlorine (Cl). And as the giant supersonic passenger planes cruise through the stratosphere, they release quantities of the chemical nitric oxide (NO), which is one atom of nitrogen bonded to one atom of oxygen.

Both the chlorine and the nitric oxide find their way into the layer of gases in the stratosphere called the ozone layer. Ozone is a special form of oxygen that has three (O_3) instead of two (O_2) atoms.

The ozone layer provides a natural protective shield against the high-energy ultraviolet radiation from the Sun. With a thinning of the ozone layer, humans run a higher risk of skin cancer, eye cataracts, and damaged immune systems. Yields of agricultural crops decrease, touching off famines. Larval forms of some marine life are destroyed, upsetting a basic link in the oceanic food chain. And, a slight warming of the atmosphere takes place.

ONE ATOM, FROM A DINOSAUR TO YOU

How Atoms Get Around

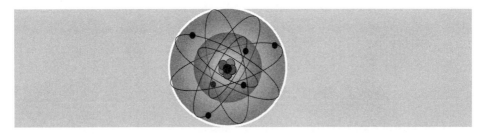

1. Virtually all living creatures contain secondhand carbon atoms that keep getting recycled year after year, century after century.

2. About 100 million years ago a dinosaur dies, and its remains decay. Its atoms are freed to combine with other atoms in the ground, air, and water. Some of its carbon atoms end up in a coal formation exposed to the ground.

3. A seed of a grass plant falls on the layer of coal and establishes roots within the coal. The plant's roots take up a molecule of carbon dioxide formed when one carbon atom of the dinosaur combined with two oxygen atoms of water. The carbon atom is next recombined as part of a molecule of the sugar glucose.

4. A rabbit eats the blade of grass containing the carbon atom of the dinosaur. The atom is again recombined, this time into a protein molecule that is part of the rabbit's backbone.

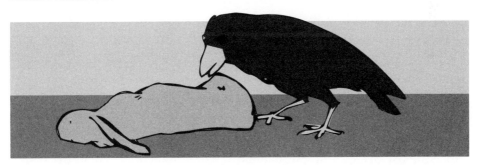

5. The rabbit dies and its remains are consumed by birds, insects, and bacteria. The carbon atom of the dinosaur is taken in by a bacterium. The bacterium dies, and the atom of carbon is next taken up as a molecule of carbon dioxide by a spinach plant.

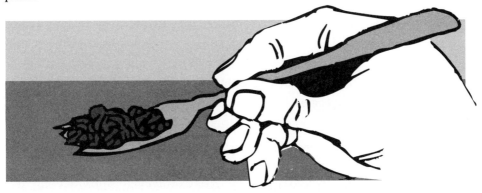

6. You eat the particular spinach leaf that contains the carbon atom of the dinosaur that died 100 million years ago. Nature is the ultimate recycler. In its ecological dictionary there is no such entry as waste.

Warnings about damage to the ozone layer were first sounded in 1974, but some members of the scientific community were skeptical of just how serious the situation might be. Then in 1985 scientists discovered a leak in the ozone layer over Antarctica, a gaping hole as large as the United States. It is now certain, according to atmospheric chemist James Anderson of Harvard University, that "there would be no ozone hole without CFCs [the class of chemicals known as chlorofluorocarbons]."

In 1991 the Environmental Protection Agency (EPA) announced that the ozone problem is far worse than anyone had thought. According to the Agency's William Reilly, ozone loss over the United States since 1978 has amounted to 4 to 5 percent. Loss over Sweden, which is at a higher latitude, is 8 percent. According to Reilly, ozone layer loss over the United States can be expected to cause 200,000 deaths from skin cancer during the next fifty years. (For every 1 percent loss of ozone we can expect a rate increase in skin cancer cases of about 5 percent.) That death rate estimate is twenty-one times higher than the EPA's earlier forecast. And it is expected to climb, because ozone layer loss is predicted to increase about 12 percent over the next twenty years. The EPA further warns that if nations do not agree to reduce the use of CFCs, an estimated three million people either alive today or born before 2075 may be killed by exposure to ultraviolet radiation.

The chlorofluorocarbons account for 25 percent of America's greenhouse emissions, according to a National Academy of Sciences report issued in 1991. The two most common are $CFCl_3$ and Freon (CF_2Cl_2). Once they enter the atmosphere, $CFCl_3$ emissions have a lifetime of sixty-four years, and Freon has a lifetime of 108 years. Eventually, both gases are carried aloft into the stratosphere where, broken down by ultraviolet radiation, they release their chlorine. The free chlorine then attacks and breaks down ozone into ordinary oxygen. In doing so it releases the chlorine, which can then attack other ozone molecules. Other CFCs are widely used in polyurethane foam seat cushions, in building insulation, and as agents for cleaning metal, sterilizing medical equipment, and fast-freezing foods.

The gas nitrous oxide (N_2O), another ozone destroyer, is produced by the use of nitrogen fertilizers. It is projected that use of these industrially produced fertilizers will increase by hundreds of percent over the next twenty-five or so years in order to feed an ever-growing number of people. Continued destruction of the ozone layer, according to a report of the National Research Council (NCR), also increases the threat of "drastic" climate changes.

Can anything be done to stop the destruction of the ozone layer? In 1987, twenty-four nations agreed to cut their production of CFCs in half by the year 2000. In June 1991, alarmed by increased damage to the ozone layer, more than ninety countries proposed banning CFCs entirely by the year 2000. China and India both objected, saying that their economies would be crippled. Because of the long life of ozone-destroying chemicals already in the atmosphere, and the amounts that will be added over the next twenty years, it may already be too late to reverse the problem. Some experts think that the high levels of chlorine now in the air will remain until the twenty-second century, possibly longer. If CFCs were banned completely tomorrow, it might take one hundred years to regain the ozone already lost.

Atmospheric physicist Michael Oppenheimer of the Environmental Defense Fund says, "Current ozone depletion is effectively irreversible. . . . Now it looks like the strong measures we're about to take won't be enough." All we can do now is sit back and wait to see what happens in the most far-reaching chemistry experiment ever carried out on living organisms.

CARBON DIOXIDE AND WORLD CLIMATE

Among the atmosphere's greenhouse gases that trap long-wave heat radiation, the most effective is carbon dioxide. Other such gases that play a lesser role include CFCs, methane, water vapor, and nitrous oxides. The burning of fossil fuels and the slash-and-burn method of clearing land in some Third World countries have tripled the amount of carbon dioxide in the atmosphere since 1950. The amount of methane has doubled since 1850.

The rising concentrations of greenhouse gases point to a gradual warming

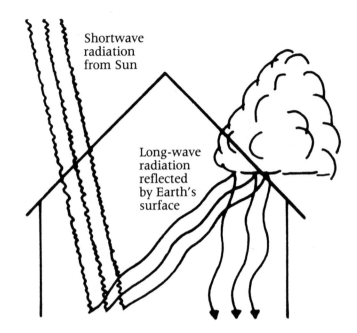

Shortwave radiation striking Earth's surface is absorbed and reemitted as long-wave (heat) radiation. This long-wave radiation is reflected by clouds back to Earth's surface. The same thing occurs in a greenhouse, where the glass roof permits the passage of shortwave radiation but traps the long-wave radiation.

of Earth's surface by 1.5 to 4.5°C over the next fifty years or so. Although such "small" amounts of temperature rise may not seem like much, they are enough to cause the polar ice caps to begin to melt, causing a slow rise in sea level that would threaten many of the world's coastal cities. Some experts forecast that sea level will rise four feet by the year 2050. This warming also would speed the pace of desert spreading in some regions, with devastating effects on crop yields.

Until the machines of industrial nations began overloading the atmosphere with carbon dioxide, about half of it remained in the atmosphere and the remaining 50 percent was absorbed by the oceans and forests, especially tropical forests. Each year since 1980, according to the United Nations Food and Agricultural Organization (FAO), an area the size of Pennsylvania has been deforested in the tropics. Since 1980 about 1.2 billion people have been meeting their needs for fuel wood by cutting down trees faster than the trees can be replaced. In Africa alone about 100 million people are suffering shortages of fuel wood and would continue to even if they cut down every tree in sight. And the situation becomes worse as Africa's population grows rapidly. On a global level, according to the FAO, 2.4 billion people will be cutting down trees for fuel wood by the year 2000.

Some scientists say that the drought that gripped the United States in 1988 probably marked the beginning of a warming trend due to the buildup of carbon dioxide and other greenhouse gases. In April 1991 the National Academy of Sciences reported that use of the atmosphere as an industrial sewer could raise global temperatures 2°F to 9°F in the near future. If so, by the year 2030 New York may be getting 48 days of summer heat above 90°F instead of 15 days; Chicago 56 instead of 16; Dallas 162 instead of 100; and Los Angeles 27 instead of 5. Part of the heat felt in the world's large cities comes from these "heat islands" themselves—from heat absorbed and stored by buildings and then reradiated, from automobile en-

Cities usually are warmer than the neighboring suburbs by an average 1° to 2°C (about 2° to 3°F). They are warmer because their extensive areas of asphalt and concrete absorb and store heat. Dust and smoke in the city air tend to collect and form a "dust-dome," which gives a city its own local climate. The dome persists until broken up by wind or rain. (*After W. Lowry*)

gines, from a city's "canyon geometry," which reduces air circulation, and from the replacement of trees and other vegetation with stone and glass.

Climatologists look for trends as possible pointers to climate change. A buildup of greenhouse gases in the atmosphere is one such trend that has been occurring for well over a century. The hottest four years of any decade since 1900 occurred during the 1980s. On the basis of the present warming trend, NASA's climatologist James Hansen has said that he is "99 percent" certain that the greenhouse effect has started. "It has been detected and is changing our climate now," he told a U.S. Senate committee hearing as early as June 1988.

The warming will have different effects in different parts of the world. Shifting wind patterns might increase rainfall over parts of Africa that are presently relatively dry, for example. Growing seasons might be lengthened in parts of the former Soviet Union, Canada, and Scandinavia. The United States might be less lucky; with 40 percent less rainfall than now its wheat and corn belts will dry up. Water tables in such regions will lower, and the water supplies for regions along the coasts will become useless as they are invaded by salt water.

Can anything be done to slow the buildup of greenhouse gases? Today we are adding to the atmosphere's carbon dioxide reservoir at the rate of 4 percent a year. Many experts say that we must try to slow that rate. If we could slow it to 2 percent a year, the big heat might not come until the year 2050. That twenty-year delay would give us time to breed new crops capable of tolerating heat and drought, redesign and rebuild selected port cities, and relocate endangered coastal populations inland. At this stage of our limited knowledge, about the only thing that seems certain is that we have just entered a new era of planetary warming.

WHEN IT RAINS ACID

Acid rain is any form of precipitation—fog, rain, snow, sleet—that contains high levels of acid. It is caused when precipitation picks up sulfur compounds released from active volcanoes and the chimneys of power plants and factories that burn low-quality coal. The caustic rain is also caused when clean rain picks up nitrogen emissions from automobile exhausts, power plants, and from other sources. As with carbon dioxide, sulfur and nitrogen emissions have been entering the air in large quantities ever since the Industrial Revolution in 1850.

Acid rain has killed many lakes and streams of the northeastern United States as well as throughout northern Europe and parts of the former Soviet Union and stunted forest growth since at least in the 1970s. Although some scientists say that acid rain has lessened somewhat since around 1980, others do not agree. No matter who is right, the amount of acid rain falling into our lakes, streams, and forests depends on how rigorously environmental protection regulations are enforced.

Chemists use a scale called pH to measure the acid in a solution. The lower the number (from 1 to 7), the greater the acidity. Glacial ice that formed long before 1850 has a pH above 5, about the acidity of milk and saliva. In February 1979 the average pH of rain in Toronto was 3.5; in the fall of 1981 fog in Los Angeles had a pH of 2.2. Wheeling, West Virginia, holds the record with a pH of 1.4. Battery acid has a pH of 1.0.

Acid rain is produced mainly by industries in the Midwest and is carried eastward by the prevailing westerly winds and deposited onto parts of Canada and the Northeast. Acid rain is destructive: By 1975 more than 80 of 214 high-altitude lakes in the Adirondacks had lost all their fish (half the lakes had a pH of 5 or lower). By the late 1970s nine rivers in Nova Scotia, once abundant with salmon, had a pH lower than 4.7 and no salmon. Acid rain has also severely damaged forests of spruce, pine, aspen, and birch in Germany and elsewhere in Europe.

The case of acid rain is one positive example of how strictly enforced regulations can aid the environment. According to Robert Repetto of Washington's World Resources Institute, "Despite increasing evidence of damage to forests and lakes from acid deposition, rain's acidity and atmospheric concentrations of sulfates and nitrates have not been increasing during the 1980s. The direct cause of these trends is the enforcement of environmental regulations limiting emissions from motor vehicles, industries, electric utilities, municipalities, and other major pollution sources."

The release of harmful substances into the environment raises an important moral question: What right does any manufacturer, industry, state, or nation have to pollute the air when that pollution is carried on the wind, crossing state and national boundaries and adversely affecting millions of people helpless to correct the situation? Several paper companies in Maine, for instance, are permitted by the state to release from their stacks noxious and corrosive fumes that have a strongly offensive odor. Usually vented after dark when they cannot be seen, the irritating fumes are carried as a huge invisible cloud that drifts on the wind from a Westbrook mill near Portland throughout the city, bringing discomfort to tens of thousands of people. Neither surgical masks nor closed windows are an effective defense.

OCEAN AND COASTAL POLLUTION

From pole to pole and from the beaches far out to sea, the oceans are polluted and getting worse, although the open ocean remains relatively clean except for plastic debris and floating tar found mainly in shipping lanes. Because most of the pollution originates on land, the coastal areas tend to be the dirtiest. But it is just those areas that contain most of the ocean's living organisms. Each year billions of tons of industrial wastes, chemicals, oily runoff from city streets, silt, and sewage flow into the sea from the land.

In order of importance, the major pollutants are nutrients from human sewage, plastics from trash disposal at sea, pesticides and industrial chemicals, and oil from tanker spills and careless tanker management. As medical wastes wash up onto our beaches, toxic chemicals and disease-causing germs accumulate in shellfish.

In 1990 a United Nations group of scientists issued a joint statement saying: "We fear, especially in view of the continuing growth of human populations, that the marine environment could deteriorate significantly in the next decade unless strong, coordinated national and international action is taken now."

Pollution can result in a process called eutrophication which occurs when a large parcel of water contains too many nutrients. The nutrients come from the runoff of sewage and the fertilizer flushed from the land. The important nutrients in these wastes are nitrogen and phosphorus, which cause the rapid growth—called a "bloom"—of algae and other water plants. When the plants die, the decomposers (bacteria) use up the water's oxygen supply and thereby cause fish kills. In the United States, oxygen-starved coastal waters are most serious along the southern coast of Louisiana, in the Chesapeake Bay, and in the New York Bight. The Pacific coast is relatively free of killer blooms.

In many parts of the world that lack sewage systems, the people use coastal beaches and rivers and streams as open toilets. The list of diseases caused by human waste contamination is long—amoebic dysentery, cholera, typhoid fever, hepatitis, and viral gastroenteritis, to name a few. Some of the disease-causing germs can live and remain infectious for as long as seventeen months. People contract these diseases by bathing in contaminated water or by eating shellfish and other seafood that have become contaminated. Areas with large concentrations of people are contaminated most frequently. But less crowded coastal areas also may be contaminated. For example, sewage is leaked or pumped directly into the sea along stretches of the Maine coast; as a result, clamming is prohibited on those shores.

In Europe, only 72 percent of the population is served by sewage treatment. In Greece the figure is 25 percent. Few large cities in West and Central Africa treat their sewage at all, and there is no toilet system whatever for most city dwellers. In Australia and Latin America, disposing sewage into the ocean is the rule, and a growing major concern.

Plastic materials, including six-pack rings and plastic bags, and discarded fishing gear such as worn or torn nets are serious sources of contamination that endanger marine mammals. Around the world, porpoises, Hawaiian monk seals, and Aleutian fur seals become entangled in discarded nets and drown. Birds, turtles, whales and other animals routinely die as a result of eating plastic debris.

Each year about 3.2 million tons of oil from municipal and industrial discharges and oil spills enter the marine environment. About 25 percent of the 55,000 tons of pesticides used in South Asia alone end up in the oceans. Although metals from industry routinely are dumped into the sea—mercury and lead are the most toxic—they are considered a minor hazard. "Hot spots" near industrial plants are exceptions, however, because the metallic pollutants are highly concentrated and dangerous.

In general, ocean pollution is difficult to document, and control is hard to achieve because both national and international actions are required.

NUCLEAR WASTES DISPOSAL

The most lethal and widespread pollutants are the radioisotopes from nuclear weapons tests and the long-lived radioactive wastes generated by the governments in the name of "national security" and the nuclear power industry.

When nuclear weapons are detonated, the resulting radioactive particles enter the atmosphere and are carried far and wide by the global circulation of winds. The radiation from nuclear power plants is released into the plants' coolant water, which then re-enters a river or a marine ecosystem. Nuclear power plants also release radiation into the atmosphere through their stacks, and into the environment when their radioactive wastes are periodically collected and either processed or buried in radiation graveyards. Ultimately, a significantly large proportion of the radiation released by human activity finds its way into the numerous biogeochemical pathways.

Radioactive iodine, for example, a product of nuclear warheads or bombs, may be carried far from the test site and contaminate large areas of vegetation. Plants incorporate it in their tissue and pass it on to grazing animals, which in turn pass it on to humans through milk consumption. This particular isotope concentrates in thyroid tissue and can disturb the function of that gland. A number of young people native to the Marshall Islands when an atomic bomb was tested on Bikini showed retarded growth because their thyroid glands were harmed by radioactive iodine.

Two other radioactive elements—radioactive cesium and radioactive strontium—also are released by nuclear weapons explosions and nuclear power plants. These products enter the food chain and work their way up to the level of human consumers. They have half-lives of thirty and twenty-eight years respectively, meaning that half a given amount of radioactive cesium, for instance, decays in thirty years, half of the remaining amount in an additional thirty years, and so on. Radioactive cesium behaves chemically like potassium and builds up in muscle tissue. Radioactive strontium behaves like calcium and is concentrated in milk and bone.

Eskimos living in northern Alaska have absorbed especially high concentrations of radioactive fallout from weapons tests. At first this finding was puzzling, because the air over the Arctic was thought to contain less fallout than regions farther south. The puzzle was soon solved when the food chain was examined. At the plant level, lichens absorbed and concentrated the fallout. Caribou ate the lichens and further concentrated it. In turn the caribou passed it on to the Eskimos, who concentrated the fallout still more. In the lichen-caribou-Eskimo food chain, the caribou had three times the concentration of radioactive cesium[137] as the lichens, and the Eskimos had twice the concentration of the caribou. The long-term effects of this radiation are unknown. Unwittingly, the Eskimos have become experimental subjects, and we now have a moral obligation to observe and protect them. But what about the others our radiation garbage has affected? Do we have a moral obligation to observe and protect them also? These are hard questions to answer.

When it comes to knowledge about the long-term effects of radioisotopes released into the environment, we are babes in the woods, which is why many biologists and medical researchers express profound concern over the development of an international nuclear industry. We have not yet learned how to make our long-lived radioactive garbage harmless, yet we continue to generate more and more of it.

For years the Rocky Flats (Colorado) Department of Energy (DOE) facility made plutonium triggers for nuclear weapons. And for years, the DOE and its contractor Rockwell International Corporation kept secret their long lists of breakdowns and biohazards. In August 1989 the DOE admitted the scandal and estimated that a cleanup of its radioactive mess would take several years and cost taxpayers up to $150 billion.

Why the fuss over plutonium? Plutonium has a half-life of not 24 years, but 24,000 years, and it is perhaps the most dangerous cancer-causing agent known. When inhaled, plutonium causes death. When plutonium enters the body through skin wounds it can produce cancers of the liver, lymph nodes, or bones. Because of such health hazards, plutonium and certain other radioisotopes must be kept far away from people for a *very* long time. Of the dozens of radioisotopes produced by a nuclear reactor, some have a half-life decay rate measured in days. Others, such as uranium^{238}, thorium^{234}, and plutonium^{239}, linger in their dangerous radioactive state for thousands of years, outliving governments and civilizations. What happens to all this radioactivity? Where does it go?

Much of it is shipped by truck or rail to special plants that treat radioactive wastes. Some of those plants extract only plutonium and unspent uranium. Tens and hundreds of thousands of gallons of radioactive liquids are then injected into the ground through shafts or are permitted to seep into the ground through huge trenches dug along geologic faults. Radioactive wastes—so hot that they keep boiling from their own heat for long periods— are stored by the federal government in giant tanks.

More than 100 million gallons of this lethal radioactive slush are now held in more than 200 tanks by the federal government at its Hanford, Washington, facilities, in South Carolina, Idaho, and Illinois. The government hopes to solidify these liquid wastes, after several years of cooling, and then bury them . . . somewhere. The Department of Energy (DOE) is now considering nine possible burial sites and hopes to start filling one of them before 1998.

Meanwhile we are told by the U.S. Public Health Service that by 1995 about two billion gallons of government-licensed radioactive stew will be merrily boiling away in storage tanks. The tanks hold from 300 thousand to 1.3 million gallons each. Some of the radioactive materials will require containment in isolation for centuries; plutonium wastes will require nearly half a million years. One gallon of that waste is enough to threaten the health of several million people. In 1970 one of the government's giant tanks leaked 60,000 gallons into the ground before the leak was discovered. At least two other tanks have sprung leaks, and leaks have been suspected in several more.

The inability of scientists and technologists to agree on questions about the safe storage of radioactive wastes—if there is such a thing as "safe" storage—has engendered more public confusion than debate. For example, does our current state of knowledge in the earth sciences allow us to reliably predict geologic activity over the next half million years? Do geologists accurately understand the long-term, heat-resisting properties of salt, shale, the deep ocean floor, or the Antarctic ice? All of those places have been considered as storage tombs. Can materials experts and engineers design containers strong enough to resist corrosion from both their external environment and their internal load of radioactive wastes? The people who are aware of these and other problems related to radioactive waste disposal are very concerned that we don't have reliable answers to *any* of those questions.

By the year 2000 our grandchildren will be faced with looking after six billion curies of strontium-90, to mention only one long-lived radioisotope. One curie of strontium-90 can kill a human being. Tens of billions of curies of other isotopes, stored in the unstable nuclei of atoms, will linger for hundreds and hundreds of thousands of years. Unlike a rainbow, they do not just go away. What would we think of an ancient civilization, now extinct, that left us such an inheritance, a civilization lacking the ability to protect future generations from the deadly wastes it irresponsibly generated, and was heedless of its children yet to be born?

OUR VANISHING FORESTS

Of all living matter on Earth's land, 95 percent consists of trees and other green plants. The bulk of that vegetation is stored in the world's vanishing tropical forests. Under the hand of man, the forests are shrinking each year at the rate of about forty to fifty million acres, an area nearly as big as the state of Washington.

The agents of destruction include expanding agriculture, logging, cattle ranching, mining, the desperate need for firewood in Third World countries, and development. According to a National Geographic Society report, "Half of Earth's rain forests have already been demolished, and experts predict that most of what is left will be gone in fifty years or less. With them will vanish a quarter of all life forms—including, perhaps, a plant that could provide a cure for cancer or help end world hunger." The world's ravenous appetite for wood is not new, although the pace at which a growing world population feeds its hunger for wood is new. Since 1960 the world demand for wood has skyrocketed 90 percent, and it is increasing daily.

Fuel has long been one of the chief uses of wood, and it continues to be today in many parts of the world. In six countries of Africa, 85 percent of the total energy used comes from wood. The average figure for the Asian nations of China, India, Indonesia, and Nepal is 52 percent. The average figure for Brazil, Costa Rica, Nicaragua, and Paraguay is 42 percent. According to the United Nations Food and Agricultural Organization, by the year 2000 the number of people in tropical Africa, tropical Asia, and tropical America who will no longer have wood for fuel, or will be using firewood faster than it can be replaced, will double to 2.4 billion people.

During the past fifty years, deforestation, coupled with overgrazing and long periods of drought, has caused the desert in the Sahel to creep over an area the size of Texas and Oklahoma. Today forested areas of the Sahel region either are gone or are quickly fading. Niger's forests have decreased 30 percent since 1970 and may vanish in another twenty-five years. Across the entire Sahel, over-cutting has reduced the region's forested area by more than half since 1950.

Today, every minute of the day and night, almost 100 acres of rain forest fall to the chain saw or are recklessly destroyed by the bulldozer's blade. Many experts fear that most of the remaining rain forests will be gone by the year 2040. The devastation of Thailand's forest was so bad between 1985 and 1988 that deforested hillsides caused landslides that destroyed the homes of 40,000 people. Thailand lost 45 percent of its rain forests between 1961 and 1985.

Acreage of a prized family of tall trees—the dipterocarps—in the Philippines shrank from 40 million in 1960 to 2.5 million in the 1980s. Most of the remaining trees stand in remote hill regions and probably will be gone by the mid-1990s. Although logging continues in some parts of the Philippines, it has been stopped in most provinces. The Philippines lost 55 percent of its rain forests between 1960 and 1985. Much of the forest destruction has been in critical watershed areas, vital areas that collect and store fresh water. Cutting on watershed mountain slopes is especially destructive, because it causes erosion as water from heavy rains cascades down the barren slopes instead of collecting in the watershed areas. The flood of downslope water collects soil, which flows into and clogs irrigation canals. The rapid storm runoff also floods inhabited lowland areas. And because the watersheds have been disturbed, there is a shortage of fresh water during the dry season.

Seventy-five percent of the forests in Africa's Ivory Coast have been cut or burned since 1960. Virtually all of the wood was wasted, representing a loss of about 5 billion dollars. In Ghana the figure is 80 percent, and a scant 15 percent of the timber was harvested before the land was cleared for agriculture. As in the Ivory Coast, most of the forest destruction in Brazil is caused by slash-and-burn farmers clearing the land. Brazil's estimated loss in burned woodlands may be 2.5 billion dollars a year. As long ago as 1980, less than half of Peninsular Malaysia's primary rain forest remained. Malaysian environmentalists fear that virtually all their remaining forest will be gone by the time their children are grown. All the primary rain forests in India, Bangladesh, Sri Lanka, and Haiti have been cut. According to the World Resources Institute, 29.7 million acres of tropical forest were destroyed in eight countries during one year—1987.

Many people who express concern over the rapid disappearance of the world's tropical rain forests suppose that most of the trees are used as timber. In many cases, the reckless use of tractors and other logging equipment destroys 50 to 75 percent of the trees that are not cut. The manager of one logging operation in Indonesia said that his men take out only about four trees per acre. In the process the forest canopy is destroyed, and about one-sixth of the trees cut down for timber are so damaged they are left behind to rot. Ecosystem destruction rarely is a concern of logging companies. Their approach almost always is to clear-cut an area, take out the timber of value to them, and leave the land in shambles.

Practically all of the mahogany, teak, and other prized hardwood logs in the world come from tropical rain forests. The rain forests also supply about 20 percent of all industrial wood—wood for plywood, pulp, house construction, paper, cardboard boxes, throw-away chopsticks, and disposable baby diapers, for example. The demand for fine hardwood is sixteen times greater today than it was in 1950. The demand for industrial wood also has skyrocketed since 1960. And as world population increases, the demand for wood will increase.

Brazil's Amazonia contains half of the world's tropical rain forests. The forests grace a region ten times the size of Texas and provide a spectacle of wilderness beyond the imagination of a city dweller. Only about 10 percent of Brazil's rain forests have been cut to date, but cutting goes on at an uncontrolled pace. Slash-and-burn farming is the leading cause of tropical rain forest destruction in Brazil and in the rest of the world. In slash-and-burn farming, an area is clear-cut and burned to open space for agriculture.

Although population growth in developed nations shows signs of slowing, it continues at an unprecented rate in most Third World nations (Indonesia is one exception). Those nations, the custodians of the world's tropical rain forests, look on their tropical rain forests as the most immediate and most promising source of desperately needed income.

At a 1988 conference in Toronto, Canada, dealing with "The Changing Atmosphere," an African delegate said that he didn't want the Western World, technologically developed and rich, to preach to him about what he could do with his trees or what he might be planning in the way of developing his nation. He added that, indeed, it was the turn of his and other Third World nations to develop and generate their share of wealth and the good life. The environment, he said, would just have to be secondary, as it was when the West grew rich by launching the Industrial Revolution.

WHERE ARE WE NOW?

During the Reagan and Bush administrations, many Americans came to believe that the federal government chose to protect industrial polluters rather than regulate them in order to protect the environment, on which all of us ultimately depend for a desirable quality of life, and for survival itself. The Reagan administration responded to repeated warnings about acid rain and to warnings about global warming with indifference. Almost always the answer was that "more research is needed." Such attitudes were merely a means of delaying, or avoiding, pollution controls, because such controls would require industry to spend money that it did not want to spend.

As an already overpopulated world continues to develop technologically and industrially, our factories and power plants knowingly or unthinkingly pour toxic substances into the biosphere. The controls that are applied rarely are self-imposed through any sense of environmental conscience. Instead, they have to be forced upon the polluters by state or federal law.

At least since biblical times people have regarded the degradation of nature as their privilege. The health of the environment has always been second. Unfortunately, that attitude is still with us, presenting the real problem that must be addressed—the birth of a collective environmental conscience based on the realization that the welfare of human beings is linked to the health of the environment.

Environmentalists the world over have been the first to develop an environmental ethic. But the values on which that ethic is based have encountered industry's hostility. The world market has yet to be mobilized to act voluntarily to preserve the environment. To change our collective ways will require a clearly stated set of environmental global values echoed over and over again by our leaders, our institutions, and the media. If we are to change many of our more destructive and wasteful living habits in order to slow the erosion of a desirable quality of life, government policies the world over, and the world's institutions, must take the lead in initiating corrective measures, with a single voice and a single purpose. The 1992 environmental summit held in Rio de Janeiro was regarded by many as a failure. But others consider the international meeting at least a start.

Equally important is a need to raise the level of literacy in science among key people the world over. When a strong and unified voice demands respect for the environment, there will be hope for the future generations in whose good interests we must act responsibly.

FURTHER READING

BOOKS

Boorstin, Daniel J. *The Discoverers*. New York: Random House, 1983.

Bugliarello, George. *Physical and Information Sciences and Engineering*. Washington, D.C.: The American Association for the Advancement of Science, 1989.

Chandler, David. *Exploring the Night Sky with Binoculars*. La Verne, Ca: David Chandler, 1983.

Clark, Mary. *Biological and Health Sciences*. Washington, D.C.: The American Association for the Advancement of Science, 1989.

Gallant, Roy A. "Coping with the Mass Media," in *The Language of Man*, Book 5. pp. 97–103. Joseph Fletcher Littell, ed. Evanston, Ill.: McDougal Littell, 1971.

———"Science and Technology: In Search of Values," in *The Maine Scholar*. Autumn 1990, pp. 89–112.

———*Before the Sun Dies: The Story of Evolution*. New York: Macmillan, 1989.

———*The Peopling of Planet Earth*. New York: Macmillan, 1990.

———*Earth's Vanishing Forests*. New York: Macmillan, 1991.

———*Beyond Earth: The Search for Extraterrestrial Life*. New York: Four Winds Press of Macmillan, 1977.

———*Earth's Changing Climate*. New York: Four Winds Press of Macmillan, 1979.

———*The Constellations: How They Came to Be*. Revised Edition. New York: Four Winds Press of Macmillan, 1991.

Group of Experts on the Scientific Aspects of Marine Pollution (GESAMP), *The State of the Marine Environment* (United Nations Environment Programme, Nairobi, Kenya, 1990).

Montagu, Ashley, ed. *Science and Creationism*. New York: Oxford University Press, 1984.

Pringle, Laurence. *Nuclear Energy: Troubled Past; Uncertain Future*. New York: Macmillan, 1989.

———*Rain of Troubles: The Science and Politics of Acid Rain*. New York: Macmillan, 1988.

Project 2061. Washington, D.C.: The American Association for the Advancement of Science, 1989.

World Resources—1990–91. New York: The World Resources Institute, 1990.

ARTICLES

Abelson, Philip H. "Waste Management." *Science*, 7 June 1985.

Angell, Marcia. "The Right to Die in Dignity." *Newsweek*, 23 July 1990, p. 9.

Atkinson, Richard C. "Supply and Demand for Scientists and Engineers: A National Crisis in the Making." *Science*, 27 April 1990, pp. 425–432.

Baker, James N. "Keeping a Deadly Secret" (workers in federally operated uranium mines) *Newsweek*, 18 June 1990, p. 20.

Barinaga, Marcia. "Scientists Educate the Science Educators." (devising ways to get more science into the schools) *Science*, 24 May 1991, pp. 1061–1062.

Beardsley, Tim. "Parched Policy." (California's water shortage) *Scientific American*, May 1991, p. 36.

Begley, Sharon, "The Antibodies That Weren't." *Newsweek*, 1 April 1991, p. 60.

———"A Bigger Hole in the Ozone." *Newsweek*, 15 April 1991, p. 64

———"On the Wings of Icarus." (geoengineering the planet) *Newsweek*, 20 May 1991, pp. 64, 65.

Bouchard, Thomas J., et al. "Sources of Human Psychological Differences: The Minnesota Study of Twins Reared Apart." *Science*, 12 October 1990, pp. 223–228.

Bower, Bruce. "Alcohol's Fetal Harm Lasts a Lifetime." *Science News*, 20 April 1991, p. 244.

———"Teenage Turning Point." *Science News*, 23 March 1991, pp. 184–186.

Cherfas, Jeremy. "FAO Proposes a 'New' Plan for Feeding Africa." *Science*, 9 November 1990, pp. 748–749.

Cowley, Geoffrey. "Brave New Drugs." (genetic science) *Newsweek*, 14 January 1991, pp. 56–57.

Culotta, Elizabeth. "Can Science Education Be Saved?" *Science*, 7 December 1990, pp. 1327–1330.

———"Pulling Neanderthals Back Into Our Family Tree." *Science*, 19 April 1991, p. 376.

Dietz, Robert S. "Demise of the Dinosaurs: A Mystery Solved?" *Astronomy*, July 1991, pp. 30–37.

Fackelmann, K. A. "NIH Says Paper Contained Bogus Data." *Science News*, 30 March 1991, p. 196.

Gawin, Frank H. "Cocaine Addiction: Psychology and Neurophysiology." *Science*, 29 March 1991, pp. 1580–1586.

Hamburg, David A. "New Risks of Prejudice, Ethnocentrism, and Violence." *Science*, 7 February 1986.

———"Population Growth and Development." *Science*, 16 November 1984.

Holden, Constance. "Irrationality—Skeptics Strike Back." (pseudoscience and scientific literacy) *Science*, 13 April 1990, p. 165.

———"Population Is Environmental." *Science*, 11 May 1990, p. 680.

"How Kids Grow." (special issue on health, psychology, and values) *Newsweek*, Summer 1991.

Jarvik, Murray E. "The Drug Dilemma: Manipulating the Demand." *Science*, 19 October 1990, pp. 387–392.

Kerr, Richard A. "Climatologists Debate How to Model the World." (Will global warming be modest or catastrophic?) *Science*, 23 November 1990, pp. 1082–1083.

———"Yucatan Killer Impact Gaining Support." (search for the impact crater behind the 65 million-year-old extinctions) *Science*, 19 April 1991, p. 377.

———"Ozone Destruction Worsens." *Science*, 12 April 1991, p. 204.

———"New Greenhouse Report Puts Down Dissenters." *Science*, 3 August 1990, pp. 481–482.

Kormondy, Edward J. "Ethics & Values in the Biology Classroom." *The American Biology Teacher*, October 1990, pp. 403–407.

Krauskopf, Konrad B. "Disposal of High-Level Nuclear Waste: Is it Possible?" *Science*, 14 September 1990, pp. 1231–1232.

Langenberg, Donald N. "Science, Slogans, and Civic Duty." *Science*, 19 April 1991, pp. 361–363.

Lederman, Leon. "Science Literacy: A Race Between Education and Catastrophe." The 1990 Marin Buskin Memorial Lecture. Washington, D.C.: The Education Writers Association.

Linden, Eugene. "The Last Drops." (the world's shrinking fresh-water supply) *Time*, 20 August 1990, pp. 58–61.

Manzer, L. E. "The CFC-Ozone Issue: Progress on the Development of Alternatives to CFCs." *Science*, 6 July 1990, pp. 31–35.

Min-Wei Lee. "Turning Teachers on to Science." *Science*, 31 August 1990, p. 979.

Monastersky, Richard. "Married to Antarctica." (continental drift 675 million years ago) *Science News*, 27 April 1991, pp. 266–267.

Musto, David F. "Opium, Cocaine and Marijuana in American History." *Scientific American*, July 1991, pp. 40–47.

Newsom, Horton E., and Kenneth W. W. Sims. "Core Formation During Early Accretion of the Earth." *Science*, 17 May 1991, pp. 926–933.

Novel, Robert C. "There Is No Safe Sex." *Newsweek*, 1 April 1991, p. 8.

"Ozone Decreasing Over U.S." *Science News*, 13 April 1991, p. 231.

Palca, Joseph. "The Sobering Geography of AIDS." *Science*, 19 April 1991, pp. 372–373.

Peterson, Ivars. "State of the Universe: If Not with a Big Bang, Then What?" *Science News*, 13 April 1991, pp. 232–235.

Piel, Gerard. "Let Them Eat Cake." (population growth and economic development) *Science*, 26 October 1984.

Pool, Robert. "Electromagnetic Fields: The Biological Evidence." *Science*, 21 September 1990, pp. 1378–1381.

———"Struggling to Do Science for Society." *Science*, 11 May 1990, pp. 672–673.

Powell, Corey S. "Peering Inward." (Earth's interior) *Scientific American*, June 1991, pp. 101–111.

Raloff, J. "Dust to Dust: A Particularly Lethal Legacy." (dust-size air pollutants). *Science News*, 6 April 1991, p. 212.

Rathje, William L. "Once and Future Landfills." *National Geographic*, May 1991, pp. 116–134.

Roberts, Leslie. "Learning from an Acid Rain Program." *Science*, 15 March 1991, pp. 1302–1305.

———"To Test or Not to Test?" (genetic screening) *Science*, 5 January 1990, pp. 17–19.

Ross, Philip E. "Science? Nyet." *Scientific American*, June 1991, pp. 17–20.

Sai, Fred T. "The Population Factor in Africa's Development Dilemma." *Science*, 16 November 1984, pp. 801–805.

"Science's 20 Greatest Hits Take Their Lumps." *Science*, 15 March 1991, pp. 1308–1309.

Selvin, Paul. "The Raging Bull of Berkeley." (do genes account for human behavior?) *Science*, 25 January 1991, pp. 368–371.

Smith, R. Jeffrey. "Ultimate Recycling: Nuclear Warheads." *Science*, 24 May 1991, pp. 1056–1057.

Stanley, Steven M. "Extinctions—or, Which Way Did They Go?" *Earth*, January 1991, pp. 18–27.

Stark, Mark. "Turning Up the Heat on the Greenhouse." *Newsweek*, 22 April 1991, p. 69.

Thompson, Jon. "East Europe's Dark Dawn." (deadening effects of industrial pollution) *National Geographic*, June 1991, pp. 36–69.

Train, Russell E. "The Quality of Growth." (learning to live within our environmental limits) *Science*, 7 June 1974, pp. 1050–1053.

Turque, Bill, and John McCormick. "The Military's Toxic Legacy." *Newsweek*, 6 August 1990, pp. 20–23.

Underwood, Anne. "The Return to Love Canal." (toxic wastes) *Newsweek*, 30 July 1990, p. 25.

Wallich, Paul. "Of Two Minds About Privacy." *Scientific American*, June 1991, p. 27.

Walsh, John. "The Greening of the Green Revolution." *Science*, 5 April 1991, p. 25.

Wheelright, Jeff. "Muzzling Science." (government silencing of information about the Valdez oil spill) *Newsweek*, 22 April 1991, p. 10.

Ziegler, Charles E. "The Second Bottom Line." (payoff to industry for protecting the environment) *Scientific American*, August 1991, p. 112.

INDEX